PHOTOCOPIABLE ACTIVITIES TO DEVELOP GRAPHICAL INTERPRETATION SKILLS

HANDLING SCIENCE DATA

YEAR 3
SCOTTISH PRIMARY 4

PETER HARWOOD AND JOYCE PORTER

Authors	Editor	Series designer	Cover illustration
Peter Harwood	David Sandford	Anna Oliwa	Edward Eaves
Joyce Porter			
	Assistant editor	**Designer**	**Illustrations**
	Joel Lane	Anna Oliwa	Gaynor Berry

Text © Peter Harwood and Joyce Porter 2002
© 2002 Scholastic Ltd

Designed using Adobe Pagemaker

Published by Scholastic Ltd,
Villiers House,
Clarendon Avenue,
Leamington Spa,
Warwickshire CV32 5PR

Printed by Bell & Bain Ltd, Glasgow

3 4 5 6 7 8 9 0   5 6 7 8 9 0 1

British Library Cataloguing-in-Publication Data
A catalogue record for this book is available from the British Library.

ISBN 0-590-53727-X

Visit our website at www.scholastic.co.uk

Acknowledgements
The authors and publishers wish to thank:

AstraZeneca Science Teaching Trust for their funding and support of the research project on which the activities in this book are based (you can visit the AZSTT website at www.azteachscience.co.uk).

The children of Knowsley, Powys and Trafford LEAs for their help in testing these investigations in the classroom.

The National Curriculum for England 2000 © The Queens Printer and Controller of HMSO. Reproduced under the terms of HMSO Guidance Note 8.

A Scheme of Work for Key Stages 1 and 2: Science © Qualifications and Curriculum Authority. Reproduced under the terms of HMSO Guidance Note 8.

CONTENTS

PAGE	ACTIVITY TITLE	GRAPH TYPE	SCIENCE CURRICULUM REFERENCES		
			QCA UNIT	NATIONAL CURRICULUM	SCOTTISH 5–14 GUIDELINES
10	Cat food survey	Reading a pictogram	3A	Sc2: 1a, 2b	Living things: Processes of life – Level C; interaction – Level A, B
12	Growing plants	Reading a block graph (scale of 2s)	3B	Sc2: 3a	Living things: Processes of life – Levels A, B
14	Healthy eating	Interpreting a pie chart	3A	Sc2: 2b	Responsibility for health: physical health – Level C
16	How often do I brush my teeth?	Reading a block graph (scale of 10s)	3A	Sc2: 2a	Living things: Processes of life – Level C
18	What do we eat at break?	Reading a pictogram	3A	Sc2: 2b	Responsibility for health: Physical health – Level C
20	Dinosaur jigsaw	Interpreting a table of data	3A	Sc2: 2a, 5b	Responsibility for health: Physical health – Levels B, C
22	Growing plants in different places	Reading a block graph (scale of 1s)	3B	Sc2: 3a, 3b	Living things: Interaction with their environment – Level C
24	Supermarket stock	Reading block graphs (scales of 50s and 100s)	3A	Sc2: 2b	Living things: Processes of life – Levels A, B
26	How good is my cloth at mopping up water?	Reading a block graph (scale of 2s)	3C	Sc3: 1a	Taking responsibility for health – Levels B, C
28	How strong is the paper?	Plotting a block graph (scale of 100s)	3C	Sc3: 1a	Earth and space: Materials from Earth – Level B
30	Permeable rocks	Interpreting a table of data	3D	Sc3: 1d	Earth and space: Materials from Earth – Level A
32	Soil sampling	Interpreting data to complete a block graph (scale of 5s)	3D	Sc3: 1d	Earth and space: Materials from Earth – Levels B, D
34	Sieving soil	Plotting a block graph (scale of 5s)	3D	Sc3: 3a	Earth and space: Materials from Earth – Levels B, D
36	Stretching tights	Interpreting a human graph	3C	Sc3: 1a	Earth and space: Changing materials – Level C
38	Bubblegum	Plotting a block graph (scale of 5s)	3B	Sc3: 1a	Earth and space: materials from Earth – Level A, B; changing materials – Level A
40	Peter's problem	Reading a block graph (scale of 1s)	3C, 3E	Sc3: 2a; Sc4: 2d, 2e	Earth and space: Materials from Earth – Level A; Changing materials – Level A, C
42	The Solar System	Reading a block graph (scale of 100s)	3F	Sc3: 2c	Earth and space: Materials from Earth – Levels A, B; Energy and forces: Properties and uses of energy – Level C
44	Warm weather	Interpreting a table of data to produce a block graph (scale of 1s)	3F	Sc3: 2c	Earth and space: Earth in space – Level C; Energy and forces: Properties and uses of energy – Level B; Earth and space: Changing materials – Level B
46	Muffling materials	Reading a block graph (scale of 10s)	3C	Sc3: 1a	Earth and space: Materials from Earth – Levels A, B
48	Investigating different surfaces	Reading a block graph (scale of 50s)	3C	Sc3:	Earth and space: Materials from Earth – Level B
50	Reflecting light	Reading a block graph (scale of 10s)	3F	Sc3: 1a; Sc4: 3c	Earth and space: Materials from Earth – Level B; Energy and forces: Forces and their effects – Level B
52	See through or not?	Reading a block graph (scale of 10s)	3F	Sc4: 3b	Energy and forces: Properties and uses of materials – Levels B, C
54	Snakey magnets	Interpreting a pictogram	3E	Sc4: 2a	Energy and forces: Forces and their effects – Level B
56	Springy science	Reading a block graph (scale of 10s)	3E	Sc4: 2d, 2e	Energy and forces: Forces – Level B
58	Sundial	Reading a block graph (scale of 10s)	3F	Sc4: 3b, 4b	Earth and space: Earth in space – Levels A, B
60	Torch shadows	Interpreting data to draw a block graph (scale of 5s)	3F	Sc4: 3a, 3b	Energy and forces: Properties and uses of energy – Level C

INTRODUCTION

WHY HAVE BOOKS ABOUT HANDLING DATA FOR SCIENCE?

Children's education should provide them with skills that will benefit them for years to come. Against this background, children's ability to read and interpret information from graphs and charts is not only essential in science, but also in everyday life, where they are exposed to information on television, in newspapers and in magazines.

In the early days of the National Curriculum, the APU[1] examined graph work in school science. They found that children could successfully carry out many of the basic skills involved in drawing graphs and extracting information from graphs. However, most of the children failed to look for and describe patterns in their data, and did not understand the wider applications of graphs. The AKSIS project[2] revisited the use and application of graphs in school science. In their research, they found *'that over 75% of pupils' graphs were incorrectly constructed and most pupils regarded graphs as an end in themselves.'* One of the aims of the project was *'that Scientific Enquiry should develop pupils' understanding of the nature of scientific activity and the relation between data and scientific theories.'*

More recently, the OFSTED subject report on Primary Science (1999–2000) concluded that *'science skills, such as handling data, that draw upon and develop numeracy need to be improved systematically. Pupils are given sufficient opportunity to develop their science through practical activities. However their ability to interpret their results and say what they have found out is sometimes hampered by their lack of understanding of charts and graphs and lack of practice in recognising patterns in data. When they are encouraged to draw their own conclusions and are helped in this by discussion with the teacher, they show better understanding of the science and can apply it in different circumstances.'*

HOW THESE BOOKS HELP

This series of books is timely, then. They have been produced to help children develop their skills in handling data and its interpretation in science. However, these activities came about initially not from a response to OFSTED, but out of a need expressed by teachers. We have undertaken a four-year research programme, 'Developing Excellence in Primary Science', generously funded by the AstraZeneca Science Teaching Trust. This project has involved working with a wide variety of children and teachers. It was not simply an academic research project: it was soundly based in the classroom, with real teachers and real children in real teaching situations.

The research team comprised a group of experienced practitioners in class teaching, and in advisory and academic research, who have worked closely with teachers to address the difficulties of trying to teach science effectively. Working with primary children, alongside their teachers, clearly showed us that there was a need to develop children's data-handling skills in situations that the children were not familiar with. There is a strong tendency for primary children to learn science in a specific context, which can then make it difficult for them to apply their new knowledge to other situations. On seeing a data-handling exercise, children would often respond, 'I haven't done this' – referring to the context, which was not significant to simply interpreting the data.

An analysis of children's performance in the Key Stage 2 National Tests[3] concurs with the OFSTED report. It shows clearly that children experience considerable difficulty in applying their knowledge to new situations (a problem of contextualised learning) and in *describing* trends in an acceptable scientific format (although, on further questioning, the children showed an underlying ability to identify trends in data). In this series, both of these aspects of data handling are addressed, and advice is given to help you develop these skills with your class.

The activities in *Handling Science Data* aim to highlight and provide opportunities to develop those skills that are common to data-handling, as

well as showing the children activities that have a practical basis and that are similar, but not necessarily identical, to some they have already done. This should help them to develop the confidence to tackle new scenarios and look primarily at the data itself.

The essential ability to analyse scientific evidence (as highlighted in the OFSTED Reports), and to express these ideas scientifically, has also been addressed. These are typically the '–er, –er' answers in National Test papers – for example, 'the lar<u>ger</u> the force, the big<u>ger</u> the stretch'. Examples that the children can practise with are given in several of the activities in this book. While children can often recognise the trend in the data mentally, they find it difficult to express their ideas in a concise and complete way: a

common response would be, for example, 'It gets bigger' (for an elastic material being stretched) – or the children may give very roundabout descriptions from which you might have to extract the trend. To overcome this difficulty, we have devised a writing structure involving a two-line jingle, rather like the rhythm of an old-fashioned train, into which the children can fit their response. In this example, the chant would be 'the bigger the force / the greater the stretch.' This focuses the children's ideas; they quickly get used to doing it and are pleased at being able to devise their own jingles. It provides a precise and concise format for expressing their ideas – but they still have to be able to identify the trend.

ABOUT THE *HANDLING SCIENCE DATA* SERIES
HOW THE BOOKS ARE ORGANISED

Each book in this series contains at least 25 activities, each comprising a page of teacher's notes and a photocopiable children's page. Some additional photocopiable resource pages are also provided. Each activity provides data related to the curricula for life processes and living things, materials or physical processes, together with a set of questions that focus on interpreting the data.

The choice of science topics in this series has primarily been matched to the QCA's *Science Scheme of Work for Key Stage 2*, which many teachers in England are now using. However, the other UK curriculum documents have also been considered, and the teacher's notes give references for the National Curriculum in England, relevant units in the QCA's *Science Scheme of Work* and the Scottish *National Guidelines for Science 5–14*. It is intended that the activities can be used alongside any primary science scheme of work as reinforcement or revision. The level of work has also been matched to the National Numeracy and Literacy Strategies, so that the work is set at an appropriate level with suitable progression for the children in each year group.

FEATURES OF THE PHOTOCOPIABLES

The photocopiable worksheets in each book cater for a range of abilities in relation to graphical interpretation skills. On each worksheet, the questions are generally arranged in order of increasing difficulty. Some are deliberately challenging to extend the most able children. The majority of the questions are simply about interpreting the data, so the children need not have done the investigation described in order to be able to answer the questions.

Some of the questions identify the key scientific ideas that are relevant to that investigation. It is hoped that the children will have internalised these key concepts if they have already explored the topic practically. Some questions are deliberately open-ended so they can be used as extension or research exercises, and provide ideal homework material. The questions cover a range of types and include:

- taking readings from graphs
- relating data to properties
- identifying and predicting trends
- investigative skills
- graph plotting and table design
- science understanding
- visualising an investigation.

The level of language varies between the different activities, and some children may need support with reading some of the worksheets. However, the topics do require technical vocabulary, so it is important that this is introduced and reinforced through any complementary lessons. One way to do this would be to let the children carry out the investigations themselves, and then to use these sheets to provide matching practice or revision material.

The system of notation used for the quoting of units in this series is *factor/ unit,* for example temperature/°C or mass/g. This is the accepted format at all levels of science (and is recommended by the ASE), though brackets – temperature (°C) or mass (g) – are acceptable at school ages. It is good practice for children to learn to put units at the top of each column in a table when recording data. This is the mathematical justification for using the '/': everything in the column below is divided by the unit, hence */unit,* and only the numbers need to be written in the columns. Equally, when the children use spreadsheets, the software will not recognise a cell that contains both text and numbers, so the children need to remember only to use numbers.

FEATURES OF THE TEACHER'S NOTES

We feel strongly that the most valuable way to help the children engage with science is by carrying out activities that provide outcomes (which could be data or observations) around which a class discussion can take place. Almost all of the data presented here has come from actual children's work. These are tried and tested activities, although the nature of practical investigations means they do not always work as successfully each time. All of the activities carry practical advice on how to carry out the activities that underpin the data. Some of these activities will be familiar to you, others not. Don't be afraid to try them out; the children will respond to them in a positive way, and the data is much more meaningful if it is 'real'.

Even the most experienced and qualified science teachers learn new things all the time; you cannot hope to remember everything you did at school or university (even if you went to all the lectures!) Very few primary teachers have the luxury of a post-16 science education, yet they are expected to be in a position to answer a wide range of children's questions. The teacher's notes provided with each activity give the answers to the questions on the worksheets (always useful!), together with the relevant background science associated with the activity. This is to assist you in dealing with questions that, in our experience, the enquiring minds of primary children might come up with, especially if your teaching is open-ended. These notes are not intended to state what you should teach the children about any topic, but to support your knowledge so that you can internalise the concepts and then deal more effectively with the children's ideas.

ABOUT *HANDLING SCIENCE DATA: YEAR 3*

The activities in this book largely follow the topics covered in Year 3 of the QCA's *Science Scheme of Work,* and are also aimed at Levels B/C of the Scottish *National Guidelines for Science 5–14.* The majority of the graphs are pictograms and bar graphs, although line graphs are introduced. Line graphs are not included (but they do appear in *Handling Science Data: Year 4* and above). Creating pie charts is not considered appropriate for Year 3 children, due to the understanding of circle measurement and of fractions and percentages that is required. However, we have found that 7- and 8-year-olds can judge *relative* proportions from just looking at a simple pie chart, so pie charts using halves, quarters and so on are introduced.

USING COMPUTERS IN PRIMARY SCIENCE LESSONS

Children's confidence in using computers is increasing all the time. So is the availability of computers: most primary classrooms now contain one. Even so, most computer-based learning activities involve either using commercial software that provides children with interactive exercises or using the computer as a research tool. Many teachers are still not confident about using computers as an integral tool for learning science.

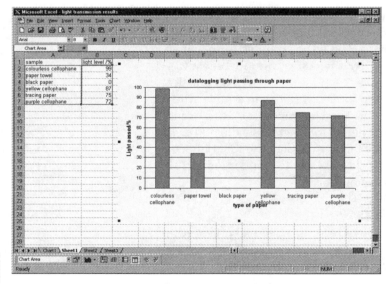

Nearly all of the activities in this series are derived from classroom investigations where, in addition to writing the results in an exercise book or a science folder, we have computerised data as a spreadsheet with a graph-plotting facility. The spreadsheet and graph can be used as a method of displaying and, more importantly, of analysing the data. Information handling and working with spreadsheets (and databases) is developed throughout the QCA's *ICT Scheme of Work* in Key Stage 2.

If the data is 'live' and on screen, children can predict the effect of changes in results on the appearance of the graph and check it instantaneously. If a result appears anomalous, the correct result can be predicted and inserted into the table and the effect observed immediately in the graph. This develops the skill of identifying trends in data – but at the same time demonstrates the value of careful measurement, which children at this age do not always readily appreciate. When they repeat the result, they will more often than not take more care (if necessary, you can intervene and discuss possible sources of error). This will develop the children's practical skills at the same time.

Each book in the series involves some examples of data collected by data-logging. This is a method of using electronic sensors to detect changes in light, temperature and sound, and then storing the data in a form that can be processed using appropriate computer software. This is specifically a feature of the QCA's *ICT Scheme of Work* in Years 5 and 6 (Units 5F and 6C).

Our research findings, reinforced by our own experiences, suggest that children are much better at interpreting graphs when the data is 'live' – for example, being plotted by the computer as the investigation is carried out.

USEFUL PRACTICAL TECHNIQUES

A 'germination sandwich' is a very good way of observing growing plants, because it is very versatile. The balsa or square beading strips are glued on with bathroom sealant, but the Perspex cover is removable. The sandwich is filled with vermiculite (available from garden centres), which absorbs water but contains no nutrients that will interfere with the investigation. Two or three seeds can be planted near the top of the sandwich, which can then be stored (perhaps in a group of several sandwiches) in a container of water, so they are very economical for space. You can't over-water the plants, and if the container is kept topped up with water they will not dry out. The plants can be carefully teased out of the sandwich to allow the roots to be observed, then replaced carefully as the investigation continues.

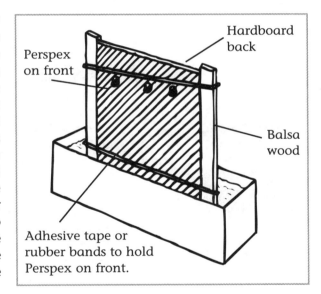

Many different factors can be investigated: seeds can be planted under different conditions (such as light, temperature, nutrients), or beans can be planted different ways up to see whether that makes a difference.

Photocopiable page 64 contains step-by-step instructions for planting seeds in a germination sandwich (see figure above). The children can follow these when carrying out an investigation.

References
1. RM Taylor and P Swatton, *Assessment Matters No.1: Graph Work In School Science* (APU, 1991)
2. A Goldsworthy, R Watson and V Wood Robinson, *Getting to Grips with Graphs, Investigations, Developing Understanding* (ASE, 2000)
3. *Standards at Key Stage 2 1996–2000* (QCA, 2001?)

CAT FOOD SURVEY

National Curriculum Science KS2 PoS Sc2: 1a, 2b
QCA Science Unit 3A: Teeth and eating
Scottish 5–14 Guidelines Living things: Processes of life – Level C;
Interaction – Levels A, B

HOW TO GATHER THE DATA

This is a good opportunity to carry out a survey since many children have pets, and this provides a change from looking at human diets. Surveying can link to maths and tally charts. Children should think carefully about what they ask: questions need a 'Yes/No' or 'Tick a box' response (not 'What does your dog like to eat?', but 'Does your dog eat x/y/z/other?' and so on).

Extension work could include discussions on gender (do male and female cats eat the same sort and amount of food?), the advantages and disadvantages of cats as pets, or the best ways of looking after them.

Leaflets about pet care and the diet of pets of different ages can be obtained from pet shops, vets or the RSPCA's Education Office (www.rspca.org.uk).

THE SCIENCE BEHIND THE DATA

For this activity, children need to be familiar with the scientific meaning of the word 'diet'. Diet is everything we eat, and a healthy (balanced and varied) diet contains the right amounts of the right foods in order to maintain our body's functions properly – in children's terms, to grow properly and keep healthy. The children need to think about different groups of foods (fruit, vegetables, meat, fish and so on), and also about starch, fat and sugar as substances found in different foods. They do not need to know terms such as 'carbohydrate' and 'protein' yet (but these appear in a lot of material they may see, so you may want to use them).

They also need to consider that different diets are appropriate for different stages of life. Some stages are obvious: babies have only milk, which provides all their dietary needs; soon this is extended to include other solids, but these are pulped because teeth are not yet developed. Growing children have different dietary needs to adults.

When discussing diet and health, it is valuable to consider how important a balanced diet and dental care is to pets as well as people. Children can use reference materials, including CD-ROMs, to find out about different pets and their diet. If possible, bring in tins of cat and dog food so the children can read the information on the labels.

In the discussion arising from the questions, it is important to cover:
■ The differences in diet between kittens, mature cats and old cats and reasons for them. Compare with humans: older cats may have lost teeth or their stomachs may be more sensitive, so more finely divided food is needed. A kitten's digestive system may not yet be fully developed so they need a different diet.

■ Most cats will normally have a diet of tinned food (for convenience), but their diet will include treats maybe once a week, such as leftover chicken from the family meal. The first survey question might therefore be better phrased as, 'What does your cat eat most of the time?'

■ Links with consumer issues can be made – why do the children think particular brands of cat food are the most popular? (Advertising?) Why do people buy supermarket own brands? (Price?)

Answers

1. 'Yummy'
2. It is the biggest 'pile' in the pictogram.
3. Fish.
4. It is the smallest 'pile' in the pictogram.
5. 5
6. It was a sensible decision. Kittens are very young – they cannot digest the same sort of food as fully grown cats.
7. Several answers are possible: older cats still eat tinned food so can be included. Children may suggest that older cats' teeth decay, so they may need softer food and should not be included. Look for a valid reason for the choice.
8. Several answers are possible. The children need to consider survey questions carefully – does their dog eat tinned food all of the time? Look for 'Yes/No' and tick/ cross question types.

Cat food survey

Some Year 3 children designed a survey to find out what pets children had and what their pets ate. They sent the survey to 40 children and found that 18 children had cats as pets. Two children kept two cats, so the total number of cats was 20. Two kept kittens, but the children decided not to include these.

The children wanted to find out what cats ate – did they eat tinned cat food or freshly cooked fish or chicken? The survey they sent out had these questions.

Pet Survey

1. Which type of pet do you have? Circle the correct answer.

Cat   Dog   Rabbit

Tropical fish   Budgie   Other

2. If you have a cat, how old is it? Please circle the correct answer.

Kitten (less than 6 months)

Mature cat (6 months – 12 years)

Old cat (over 12 years)

3. What does your cat eat? Please tick.
Tinned cat food – 'Yummy' ☐
Tinned cat food – 'Tasty' ☐
Tinned cat food – Supermarket own brand ☐
Freshly cooked or tinned fish ☐
Freshly cooked meat ☐

The results of their investigation were recorded in a pictogram.

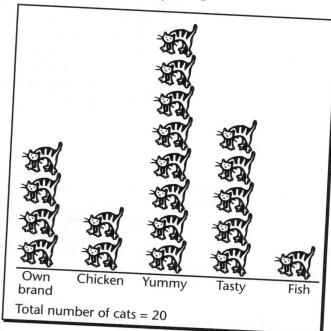

Own brand   Chicken   Yummy   Tasty   Fish

Total number of cats = 20

Questions

1. Which was the most popular cat food?

2. How did you find this out from the pictogram?

3. Which food was the least common?

4. How did you find this out from the pictogram?

5. How many cats preferred 'Tasty' cat food?

6. Do you think it was a good decision not to include the kittens in the results? Give a reason for your answer.

7. The children decided that they would include older cats in the survey – what do you think about that? Can you think of a reason why older cats might have a different diet?

8. Design a survey for dog food. Look at the questions in the cat survey – would you ask these questions? Can you think of better questions? Think about your dog or your friend's dog and what it eats.

GROWING PLANTS

National Curriculum Science KS2 PoS Sc2: 3a
QCA Science Unit 3B: Helping plants grow well
Scottish 5–14 Guidelines Living things: Processes of life – Levels A, B

HOW TO GATHER THE DATA

Often we are limited to growing cress in the classroom, but there are many other plants that can be used to illustrate growth. Growth can be measured in different ways: by height (as here), by counting leaves, or by mass (grow grass in a tray, cut it and weigh the clippings). Don't forget roots – they grow as well (onions produce a lovely root system if you grow them in the neck of a jar with just the bottom dipped in water).

As well as providing graphs for children to extract information from, plant growth can be used to trigger children's suggestions as to what else could be found out from the data. They could predict when the plant will reach a particular height; more able children could identify trends (that the rate of growth slows down eventually), and possibly make more difficult predictions, such as what the maximum height of the plant will be (not more than 25cm in this case). The data shows children the need to make careful measurements of plants growing, and that plants need water to grow.

The best way to grow plants (such as beans) for gathering data like this is to use a 'germination sandwich', which allows you to control the conditions easily. Over-watering (due to over-enthusiasm) is a problem with some children! Photocopiable page 64 contains instructions detailing how to make a germination sandwich.

THE SCIENCE BEHIND THE DATA

When a seed is planted, it needs food in order to grow. The seed itself is a store of food, with the embryonic root and shoot inside

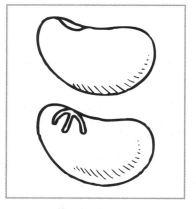

(these can be revealed if the seeds are soaked in water for 24 hours and then opened up), but this food gets used up quickly. When a seed starts to grow the root grows first, anchoring the plant and taking in water, then the shoot begins to grow. When the plant sprouts leaves above ground it can make its own food by photosynthesis. Remember that plants need food, water and oxygen all the time to carry out respiration so that they can live and grow. If light is present, green plants can photosynthesise as well, using carbon dioxide and water to make carbohydrate; this process releases oxygen. Plants can photosynthesise in some kinds of artificial light, as well as in sunlight.

Answers

1. Day 4. (More able children may say Day 3. This is fine if they can justify their answer by saying that the growth was measured on Day 4, so must have started on Day 3.)
2. Because the seed needs time to germinate, because the growth underground is not visible, or because there is not much growth before then.
3. A ruler.
4. She should water it.
5. Day 16.
6. 16cm.
7. 22cm.
8. About 23cm. (Answer should be more than 22cm, and less than 25cm.)
9. 10cm.
10. Yes, the plant will carry on growing, but it does not seem to be growing as quickly as it did in the beginning. Eventually it will not grow any taller.

Growing plants

Sau-Lang put a bean seed in some compost and watered it each day. She put it in a bright place in the classroom and measured its height every two days.

She plotted a graph of her results.

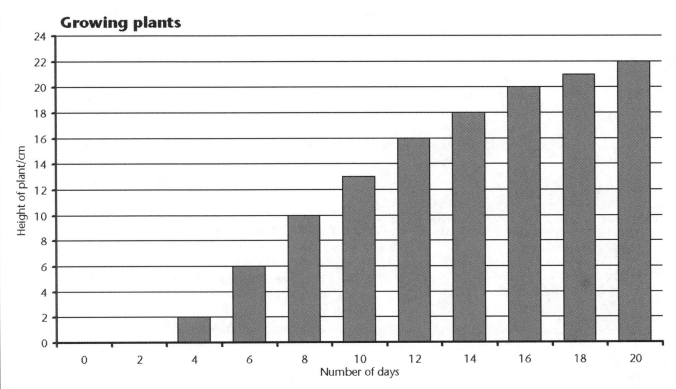

Questions

1. On what day did the plant start to grow?

2. Why do we only see it has started to grow then?

3. What can Sau-Lang use to measure the height of the plant?

4. What should Sau-Lang do every day to help the plant to grow?

5. When did the plant have a height of 20cm?

6. On Day 12, how tall was the plant?

7. Sau-Lang stopped measuring on day 20 – how tall was the plant then?

8. How tall do you think the plant was on Day 22?

9. By how much did the plant grow between Day 8 and Day 16?

10. Do you think the plant will carry on growing?

HANDLING SCIENCE DATA YEAR 3

HEALTHY EATING

National Curriculum Science KS2 PoS Sc2: 2b
QCA Science Unit 3A: Teeth and eating
Scottish 5–14 Guidelines Responsibility for health: Physical health – Level C

HOW TO GATHER THE DATA

Creating pie charts is not an appropriate activity at this level – but experience has shown that Year 3 children can interpret a chart like the one in this activity, which introduces them to the idea of a pie chart as a clock face. Children can think about what they ate yesterday and compare it with Sian's record.

The children can keep a record of their diet, using tally charts to record food eaten or designing their record as a menu.

THE SCIENCE BEHIND THE DATA

The children need to be familiar with the scientific meaning of the word 'diet'. Diet is everything we eat, and a healthy (balanced and varied) diet contains the right amounts of the right foods to maintain our body's functions – in children's terms, to grow properly and keep healthy. The children need to think about different groups of foods (fruit, vegetables, meat, fish and so on), and also about starch, fat and sugar as substances found in different foods. They do not need to know terms such as 'carbohydrate' or 'protein' yet (although these are used in a lot of material they may see, so you may want to use them).

'Recommended Daily Allowances' cannot be very specific, but a general guide for a child is 8000kJ of energy and 30g of protein, roughly in the proportion: 8 starch, 4 vegetable, 3 fruit, 3 dairy, 3 meat/fish/beans, and a small amount of fat/sweets.

Sian's 24-hour diet contained foods from each group (see below left) and is a varied diet, possibly with too much sugar. Ask the children how they would alter her diet to make it more healthy. Discuss how important it is to eat a number of foods from each group every day – particularly fresh fruit and vegetables. This can range from 'Are you having a balanced diet?' to comparisons with 'Recommended Daily Allowance' for better-informed children. (This is an ideal opportunity to bring social and cultural issues about food and diet into teaching sensitively within a science context.)

It is difficult to allocate some foods to a single group. A ham sandwich, for example, contains carbohydrate, fat and meat. Different children will appreciate this fact to different extents, so it needs to be addressed in discussion. You might like to consider the more significant elements (in a ham sandwich, the meat and carbohydrate are more significant), depending on the children's ability. This introduces a feature of scientific evidence: we are keeping it simple, but scientists would need to be more precise.

Answers

1. Foods for activity.
2. Bread, potatoes, crisps, cereal, sugar, fruit pie, chocolate, margarine, sugary drinks.
3. Foods for health.
4. Any fruit or vegetables, wholemeal bread, baked potatoes.
5. She ate foods that gave her energy (activity foods), so she would be able to play netball and tennis well.
6. She ate a good balance of the different types of foods.
7. Some of the foods she ate, such as sugary foods and drinks, are bad for your teeth if too many are eaten.
8. (Compare children's lists sensitively.)
9. Bar graph of numbers of different foods (ignoring quantities). You could add extra discussion questions at the end to do with commenting on or comparing diets.

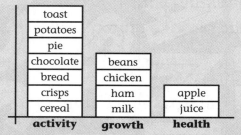

This shows the bar graph for Sian's menu. You cannot really get an exact bar graph unless you weigh the foods, but the height of the columns gives an idea of variety.

Healthy eating

Sian is trying to make sure she is eating the right foods to keep fit and healthy. She has kept a record of all the foods she ate yesterday.

Her diet needs to include:
- food for activity
- food for growth
- food for health.

She sorted out how much food she had for growth, how much for health and how much for activity. These types of foods can be displayed in a pie chart:

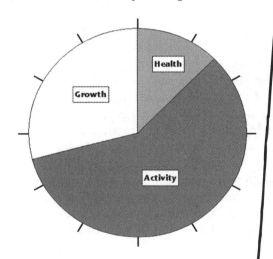

Healthy eating

This is what she ate:

Breakfast
Orange juice, bowl of sugar-coated cereal with milk, toast with margarine, cup of tea with milk.

Break
Packet of crisps.

Lunch
Two ham sandwiches, chocolate bar, apple, bottle of blackcurrant juice drink.

After school
Chocolate bar, orange squash.

Dinner
Chicken, beans, boiled potatoes, apple pie, cup of tea with milk and sugar.

Supper
Cup of hot chocolate.

Questions

1. Which type of food did Sian eat the most of?

2. Name some of the foods she ate that are in this group.

3. Which type of food did she eat the least of?

4. Name some other foods she could have eaten in this group.

5. Sian played netball at school and tennis after school. Did she eat the right sort of foods for this?

6. Explain whether or not you think Sian is eating a balanced diet.

7. Do you think the foods Sian ate were good for her teeth?

8. Make a list of the foods you ate yesterday.

9. Make a bar graph showing the different foods in your list divided into the three types of food.

HANDLING SCIENCE DATA YEAR 3

HOW OFTEN DO I BRUSH MY TEETH?

National Curriculum Science KS2 PoS Sc2: 2a
QCA Science Unit 3A: Teeth and eating
Scottish 5–14 Guidelines Living things: Processes of life – Level C;
Responsibility for health: Physical health – Level C

HOW TO GATHER THE DATA
You can easily obtain data for this activity by asking children to raise their hands according to how many brush their teeth twice a day, once a day and less than once a day, and recording answers as a tally chart on the board (this is less personal than surveying individual children). You can then discuss with the children the most appropriate method of displaying the tally chart data: using a bar chart (as here) or a pictogram.

THE SCIENCE BEHIND THE DATA
It is extremely important to brush your teeth after every meal to prevent the build-up of plaque. Plaque is a sticky bacterial substance that forms on the teeth and feeds on the sugars inside the mouth, producing acids that accelerate tooth decay. When teeth are not properly brushed, plaque builds up on the surface of teeth and irritates the gums. If this condition is left untreated, the gums will respond by pulling away from the teeth, leaving pockets that contain bacteria and pus that destroy the bone sockets that hold the teeth in place.

Acids cause tooth decay by removing the minerals from teeth. Sodium fluoride (an additive in toothpaste) and the mouth's natural saliva help to replace these minerals. Adding fluoride to toothpaste and our water supply makes our tooth enamel harder than if other compounds were used. Because the mineral is harder, it is less susceptible to attack. Chemical trials have shown that fluoride toothpastes can reduce decay by 15–30%. More about dental care can be found at www.bda-dentistry.org.uk.

The graph can reinforce work you have been doing with the children on teeth – in particular, the importance of brushing teeth regularly in order to avoid having a tooth filled or removed. If possible, ask a school nurse or health professional to visit the class to explain how the children should clean their teeth. They may be able to demonstrate the use of disclosing tablets that colour areas of the teeth that have not been brushed well (and still contain plaque) reddish-pink. This is particularly effective after a break. The colour should disappear after brushing (or better brushing).

Answers
1. 60.
2. Once a day.
3. 10. (Children may say 40 if they think once a day is not enough.)
4. (Display to show results of survey. Photocopiable resource page 63 provides ready-drawn axes on which the children can record their results.)
5. To remove any sugar, bacteria or food particles that may be present on or between the teeth. The bacteria produce acid that decays the tooth enamel. To remove plaque from the teeth.
6. Most people brush their teeth in the morning (after breakfast) and at night before they go to bed.
7. Foods that contain sugar, chocolate, sweets, sugary fizzy drinks and so on.

How often do I brush my teeth?

A national survey asked a sample of children aged between 7 and 10 how often they brushed their teeth.

The results, for the sample of 100 children, are shown in this bar chart:

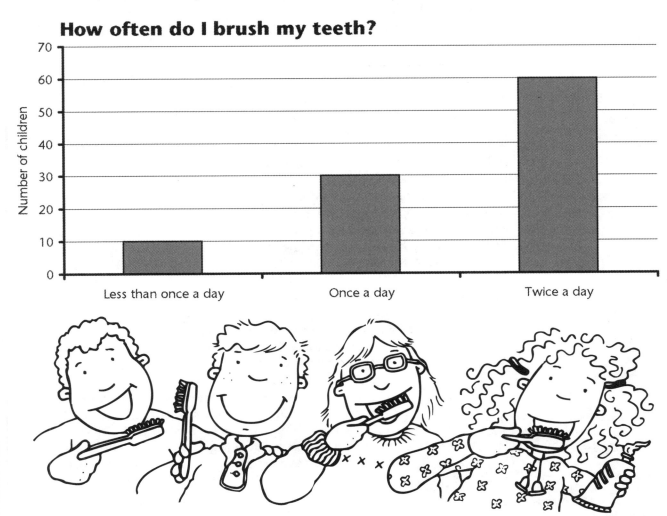

Questions

1. How many of the children cleaned their teeth twice a day?

2. How many times did exactly 30 children clean their teeth?

3. From the graph, how many of the children do you think are not brushing their teeth as often as they should?

4. Carry out a survey in your class to find out how often your classmates clean their teeth. Record your results in a bar chart on the graph paper included, or in a pictogram. Compare your results with those shown above.

5. Why do you think it is a good idea to brush your teeth twice a day?

6. When do people usually brush their teeth?

7. Name three things we eat or drink that are bad for our teeth.

HANDLING SCIENCE DATA YEAR 3

WHAT DO WE EAT AT BREAK?

National Curriculum Science KS2 PoS Sc2: 2b
QCA Science Unit 3A: Teeth and eating
Scottish 5–14 Guidelines Taking responsibility for health: Physical health – Levels B, C

HOW TO GATHER THE DATA

Children can carry out a survey of the snacks eaten on a particular day to create a large pictogram display on the classroom or corridor wall.

It is important to discuss the accuracy of the data, the sample size and appropriate generalisations. Do all classes eat the same things? If the survey were carried out across the whole school, there would be a larger number of children in the sample, and so it would be a better reflection of what primary children eat at break.

This activity could be used in relation to a 'healthy eating week', so the children can compare the snacks they normally eat at break with those eaten when they are thinking about being healthy. Discuss which foods are less damaging to teeth, such as apples and raw carrots, and whether these are as enjoyable to eat as less healthy alternatives.

THE SCIENCE BEHIND THE DATA

This survey provides many opportunities for you to begin reinforcing the idea of a varied and healthy diet, and that some foods are important for health and others for activity. The children need to be familiar with the scientific meaning of the word 'diet': diet is everything we eat, and a healthy (balanced and varied) diet contains the right amounts of the right foods to maintain our bodies' functions properly – in children's terms, to grow properly and keep healthy. The children need to talk about different groups of foods (fruit and vegetables) and about starch, fat and sugar as substances found in different foods. A balanced diet should include carbohydrates, fats, some sugar for energy, proteins for growth and vitamins for disease resistance. Snacks can make an important contribution to our diet; no food is totally unhealthy, and food should always be enjoyable.

Answers
1. Crisps.
2. Raw carrot.
3. Apples, bananas and carrots.
4. Apples and carrots.
5. Chocolate, crisps, bananas.
6. 10
7. The most likely answer is 'Yes'. A larger survey involving the whole school would provide this information. The data could be presented first class-by-class and then for the whole school.

What do we eat at break?

A class of 25 children from Parkwood Primary School carried out a survey to find out the most commonly eaten snacks at morning break.

They plotted their results on a pictogram:

Questions

1. Which is the most popular snack eaten at morning break?

2. Which is the least popular snack?

3. Which snacks in the survey would be the most healthy?

4. Which snacks would be best for looking after teeth?

5. The children have a PE lesson after morning break. Which snacks would be best for giving them energy?

6. Some children ate two things at break. How many children did this?

7. Do you think children in other classes at this school would eat similar things at break? How would you find out?

DINOSAUR JIGSAW

National Curriculum Science KS2 PoS Sc2: 2a, 5b
QCA Science Unit 3A: Teeth and eating
Scottish 5–14 Guidelines Living things: Interaction with their environment – Level C

HOW TO GATHER THE DATA

I should think every school in the country has books about dinosaurs! There are also many excellent websites (www.bbc.co.uk/dinosaurs is an excellent starting point) and the Natural History Museum (tel. 020 7942 5000; www.nhm.ac.uk) for any other information you require.

The data in this activity will need careful reading and interpretation before the children look at completing the activity. It's also an opportunity for the children to apply their knowledge about diet and teeth to unfamiliar animals.

THE SCIENCE BEHIND THE DATA

Dinosaurs are one sub-group of a group of extinct reptiles that lived from about 230 million years ago. The word 'dinosaur' was coined in 1842 by the British anatomist Sir Richard Owen, and is derived from the Greek words *deinos,* meaning 'marvellous' or 'terrible', and *sauros,* meaning 'lizard'. For more than 140 million years, dinosaurs reigned as the dominant animals on land. They died out about 65 million years ago – one theory being that a giant meteorite hit the Earth, causing a major climatic change that the dinosaurs could not survive.

Carnivorous dinosaurs had sharp teeth for tearing flesh, and shorter front legs as arms with claws for holding down their prey. The herbivores usually had four equal legs and longer necks for grazing.

Answers
Two completed dinosaur jigsaws.

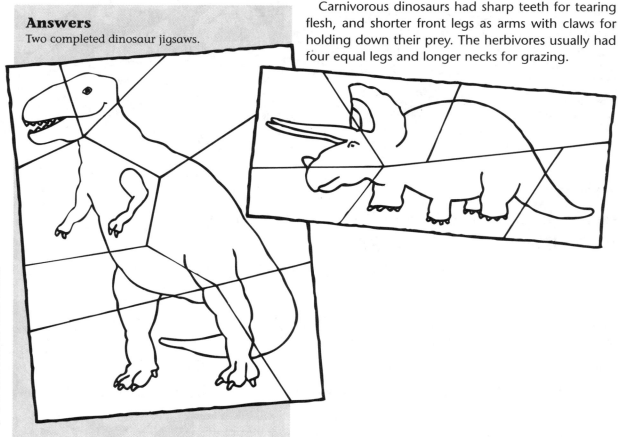

Dinosaur jigsaw

All animals, including humans, need to have a balanced diet. Their teeth are suitable for the type of diet they have. Some animals, such as cows and sheep, eat only plants, and their teeth and bodies are adapted for this. Cats and dogs eat meat, so their teeth are adapted to tear and chew meat and they have claws to hold onto their prey.

Millions of years ago dinosaurs were found all over the Earth. Some were plant-eaters and some were meat-eaters.

Part	Plant-eater	Meat-eater
	Triceratops	Tyrannosaurus Rex
Neck	Armoured	Thick
Head	Horned	Large
Jaws	Beaked	Massive
Teeth	Small, grinding	Knife-like
Tail	Short	Stiff, used for balance
Legs	4	2
Arms	0	2 small
Feet	Hoof-like	Clawed

Questions

1. Cut out the jigsaw pieces. Use the information in the table to make two dinosaurs: a plant-eater (Triceratops) and a meat-eater (Tyrannosaurus Rex).

HANDLING SCIENCE DATA YEAR 3

GROWING PLANTS IN DIFFERENT PLACES

National Curriculum Science KS2 PoS Sc2: 3a, 3b
QCA Science Unit 3B: Helping plants grow well
Scottish 5–14 Guidelines Living things: Processes of life – Levels A, B

HOW TO GATHER THE DATA

This written activity can be used to stimulate lots of questions about the growth of plants for the children to investigate – for example: *How much water does a seed need to germinate? Can you plant a seed upside-down? What type of soil is best for growing seeds?*

A 'germination sandwich' is a very good way of observing plant growth. The balsa wood strips are glued on, but the Perspex is removable. The sandwich is filled with vermiculite (which is available from garden centres); this absorbs water, but contains no nutrients that would interfere with the investigation. Not much space is needed to store the sandwiches, and they cannot be overwatered, which is useful in the classroom. Photocopiable page 64 contains a detailed diagram with instructions on how to make a germination sandwich.

If many seemingly identical seeds are planted at the same time, they will not all grow to identical heights. Data from this experiment can be used to remind the children that seeds grown apparently under the same conditions often grow to different sizes, because each seed is different.

THE SCIENCE BEHIND THE DATA

The root and shoot of a new plant use the cotyledons of the seed as a food store until it can start making its own food – by photosynthesis, which requires light. Thus a seed will germinate in the dark, as it does not need a source of light in order to start growing. The bean plant in the dark cupboard grows tall because it is seeking light (phototropism) – but as there is none, it is not stimulated to produce the green pigment chlorophyll, and so cannot photosynthesise. The effect of this is that it grows spindly and weak and the leaves are yellow, not green. The seed in the fridge does not grow at all, because it is too cold for the seed to germinate.

The plants in the cupboard and the fridge show that temperature and light have different effects on the growth of a plant: a low temperature prevents the plant from growing at all; darkness prevents the plant from making its own food and growing healthily. Although questions 8 and 9 in the activity identify putting the plant in the fridge as a mistake in terms of fair testing, it can still be used to illustrate a scienfic point: that a seed will not germinate without warmth.

Answers

1. The cupboard.
2. No, it looked yellow.
3. Because it grew taller trying to find the light in the cupboard.
4. The plants on the window and on the shelf.
5. Because they had similar amounts of light.
6. Accept sensible suggestions such as: roots prefer to grow in the dark, so they grow longer trying to find the dark; the plant is healthier so can grow a better root system.
7. Several answers are possible: use the same amount of vermiculite, the same watering patterns, similar-sized beans. The same light is not a correct answer, as this is the effect that is being changed. The ruler is the measuring instrument.
8. No.
9. The temperature was a lot lower in the fridge and plants need warmth to grow.

Growing plants in different places

Class 3 wanted to see how light affected plant growth, so they planted some bean seeds in a germination sandwich and watered them every day.

They put the frames in different places: one on a windowsill in the light, one at the back of the classroom, one in a cupboard and one in a fridge. They used a datalogger and light probe to measure the light in each place at midday.

After two weeks they measured the height of each plant.

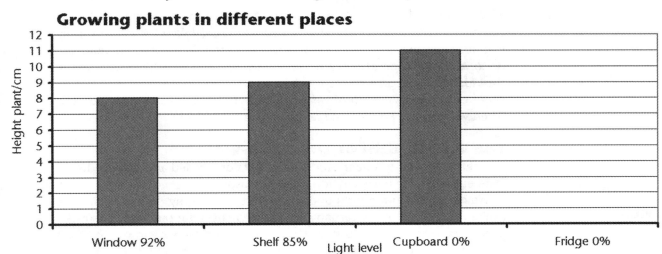

They also observed what the plants looked like.

Place	Appearance of plant
Window	Green shoot, two healthy leaves, long roots
Shelf	Green shoot, two healthy leaves, medium roots
Cupboard	Thin yellow stem, curly yellow leaves, medium roots
Fridge	No growth

Questions

1. Where did the tallest plant grow?

2. Was the tallest plant the healthiest plant?

3. Can you explain scientifically why this plant had the greatest height?

4. In which two places did plants grow to a similar height?

5. Suggest a reason why they grew to a similar height.

6. The plant in the window had the longest roots. Why do you think this was?

7. What did the children have to do to make this as fair a test as possible?

8. Do you think putting a plant in the fridge allowed a fair test?

9. Explain your answer to Question 8.

HANDLING SCIENCE DATA YEAR 3

SUPERMARKET STOCK

National Curriculum Science KS2 PoS Sc2: 2b
QCA Science Unit 3A: Teeth and eating
Scottish 5–14 Guidelines Taking responsibility for health: Physical health – Levels B, C

HOW TO GATHER THE DATA

To find information about quantities of food sold in supermarkets, try contacting your local supermarket – they are usually very helpful if you say you are a teacher and explain why you want the information. Alternatively, go to your local supermarket and carry out your own survey of what is on the shelves. You could go with the children on an arranged visit and the children could estimate how much of various food items there is, or you could do it when you go shopping if you really want to!

THE SCIENCE BEHIND THE DATA

The children need to understand the benefits of a varied and balanced diet. Different foods are necessary for different reasons.

We need food in the form of carbohydrates for energy, so that we can be active. If we take in more carbohydrate than we need for our lifestyle, any left over is converted to fat and stored as a food reserve. Fats are important food substances in their own right: they are very energy-rich and less bulky than carbohydrates. They act as an insulating material to keep in body heat, and they are important for providing fat-soluble vitamins such as vitamin D – needed for proper bone formation.

We need foods for body-building and tissue repair in the form of protein, found in meat, eggs, fish, soya and beans. Fresh fruit and vegetables are important sources of vitamins and minerals – such as vitamin C, which is important for growth and for healthy skin, teeth and gums. Fruit and vegetables also provide roughage (fibre), which provides non-digested bulk to keep waste products moving through the digestive system.

Lots of information leaflets are available from a wide variety of sources, such as local health authorities. The British Nutrition Foundation website (www.nutrition.org.uk) contains articles and resources about diet through different life stages.

Answers

1. Potatoes.
2. Apples.
3. Vegetables (1500kg vegetables, 900kg fruit).
4. By adding up all the amounts of vegetables in kg, then adding up all the amounts of fruit in kg and comparing the two. (Make sure the children know they cannot just look at the heights of the bars, because the two scales are different.)
5. Broccoli and pears.
6. Broccoli.
7. Both the bars are the same height, but the scale of the vegetables graph has higher numbers.
8. We need potatoes to give us energy (as carbohydrate). This helps us to keep active.
9. They provide vitamins (especially vitamin C) to keep us healthy, and roughage to help our digestion.

Supermarket stock

The local supermarket buys lots of fruit and vegetables each day to sell to its customers.

The amount it buys is shown in the two bar graphs below.

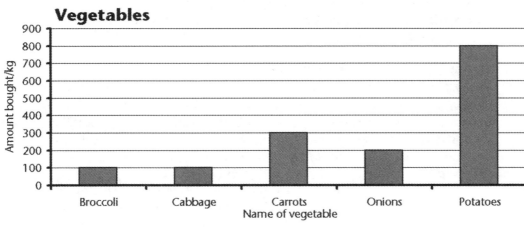

Vegetables

Amount bought/kg — Name of vegetable (Broccoli, Cabbage, Carrots, Onions, Potatoes)

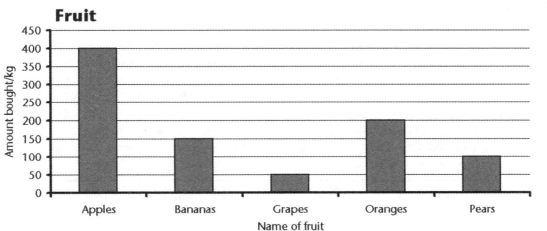

Fruit

Amount bought/kg — Name of fruit (Apples, Bananas, Grapes, Oranges, Pears)

Questions

1. Which vegetable does the supermarket buy the most of?

2. Which kind of fruit does it buy the most of?

3. Which does it buy more of each day: fruit or vegetables?

4. Explain how you worked this out.

5. What are the names of the fruit and the vegetable that the supermarket buys the same amount of each day?

6. Which does the supermarket buy more of each day: broccoli or grapes?

7. Explain how you worked this out.

8. The supermarket sells a lot more potatoes than any other vegetable or fruit. Why do we need to eat potatoes? What do they help us to do?

9. Why are fruits such as oranges good for us?

HANDLING SCIENCE DATA YEAR 3

HOW GOOD IS MY CLOTH AT MOPPING UP WATER?

National Curriculum Science KS2 PoS Sc3: 1a
QCA Science Unit 3C: Characteristics of materials
Scottish 5–14 Guidelines Earth and space: Materials from Earth – Level B

HOW TO GATHER THE DATA

You will need to assemble a range of cloths for this activity. Let the children observe the materials and feel the different textures and thicknesses. Allow them to use a wide range of their own vocabulary in an activity such as this, as well as developing their science vocabulary. For example, from children's suggestions such as *soft, smooth, hairy, spongy* or *thick*, introduce science words such as *porous, absorbent, compress* and so on.

Cut identical strips of each cloth, say 20cm × 1cm. Put each strip in a container, held firmly in place by a peg. Pour the same amount of blue coloured water into each container and leave the strips for ten minutes. Remove the strips carefully and put them on a paper towel, then measure the length of 'blueness' on each strip in centimetres with a ruler.

A story is a very popular way of introducing children to an investigation, and the following is one example that has been used successfully. Setting a context introduces children to the idea of investigating for a purpose – many scientists test materials when developing new products, and groups such as the Consumers' Association test products for value. Here, links can be made to economic understanding – 'Wonder' kitchen roll is actually inferior in this test to ordinary kitchen roll. This could lead on to a discussion about the claims made in adverts.

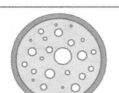

Sponge
(water fills the holes)

Tissue
(water fills the spaces between fibres)

My friend has a son called Gary, who lost his job in a chemistry laboratory because he caused a big explosion. The only job he could find was working as a cook for a Duke. The Duke's kitchens were enormous and the only way Gary could find of getting around them was to use his roller blades, but he went round the kitchens so fast that he kept spilling things. The Duke found out and told Gary that if he did not mop up all the things on the floor, he would get the sack again. Gary's mum was desperate – she went down to the supermarket and bought lots of things that would help Gary mop the floor – but she needs your help… which material is the best?

Answers

1. The sponge cloth.
2. Because it is made of sponge, which soaks up lots of water. It has spaces in it to hold the water.
3. The dishcloth.
4. The thickness of the cloth, the smoothness. (The children may suggest the colour of the water, but this won't make a difference.)
5. The ordinary kitchen roll. It offers better performance for less money.
6. Takes in water/liquid.
7. They have an open structure with spaces that take in water, or the material holds water between the fibres. (The response will depend upon the ability of the children and their experiences.)

THE SCIENCE BEHIND THE DATA

Materials that absorb water usually have quite 'open' structures so (at a simple level) the water can penetrate into the material. Some children may appreciate that water is being 'trapped' in between the fibres or pores of the material. You can see the 'open' structure of tissue paper with a good magnifying glass or simple microscope, if you have one (see diagram). More holes or spaces should allow the cloth to hold more water, so a thicker cloth would probably hold more water.

How good is my cloth at mopping up water?

A group of children are testing materials to find out how good they are at mopping up water. They have cut strips of each material that are 1cm wide and 20cm long. They dip the end in a beaker containing some blue coloured water and leave them for ten minutes. Then they take them out and measure how far the blue colour has risen up the strip.

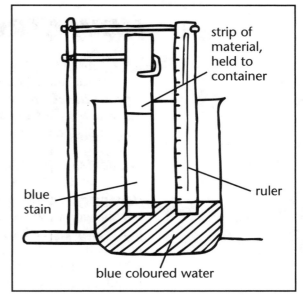

Here are their results:

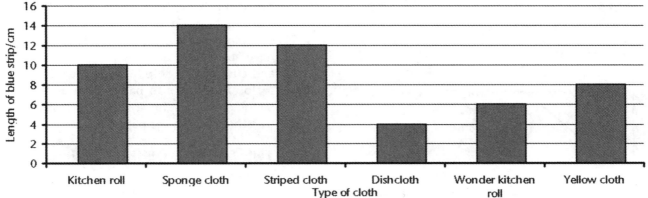

How good is my cloth at mopping up water?

Questions

1. Which material soaked up the most water?

2. Explain why this material can soak up the most water.

3. Which material soaked up the least water?

4. The children were very careful in setting up a fair test. Think carefully about the materials they were using. Name one other thing apart from the length and width of the material that could have affected the results.

5. 'Wonder' kitchen roll has been widely advertised on television as the best material for mopping up spills, but it costs £2 a roll. Ordinary kitchen roll costs £1 a roll. Looking at the results of the investigation, which material would you buy? Explain your choice.

6. What does the word 'absorbent' mean?

7. How are materials that absorb water different from those that do not?

HANDLING SCIENCE DATA YEAR 3

HOW STRONG IS THE PAPER?

National Curriculum Science KS2 PoS Sc3: 1a
QCA Science Unit 3C: Characteristics of materials
Scottish 5–14 Guidelines Earth and space: Materials from Earth –
Level B; Changing materials – Level A

HOW TO GATHER THE DATA

You could do this investigation in one of two ways – either with the whole class, predicting the strength of the various papers (cellophane, paper towel, newspaper, wrapping paper, tissue paper and so on), and carrying out the practical measurements as a shared activity for safety reasons; or as part of an open-ended whole-class activity, with different groups of children examining different papers and discussing the properties related to their uses, then investigating these properties (which is easiest to crease, strongest, most flexible or most absorbent?)

Children may need some help in deciding how to carry out each investigation. To avoid 100g masses dropping on toes, it's a good idea to have something underneath to catch and cushion the drop. Making a collar to loop around the paper strip and hanging the weights from it will stop the string tearing the paper strip.

THE SCIENCE BEHIND THE DATA

This activity helps increase children's awareness of the everyday things around them. They will all have come across different types of paper, but have probably never asked why, for instance, tissue paper is good for wrapping up things like jewellery or for making paper flowers. It's important to discuss these ideas with them, as you will also be introducing key vocabulary: the words that describe the properties of materials. 'Strength', in the scientific sense, means how easy it is to break something, so a steel knife is strong whereas tissue paper or a plastic knife are weak.

All materials are made up of 'particles'. A material's strength depends upon the strength of the forces holding the particles together. Pulling any material will force the particles apart, and when the pulling force becomes greater than the force holding the particles together, the material will break.

Answers
1. A diagram such as this:

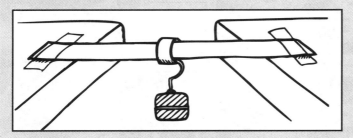

2. A bar graph similar to this:

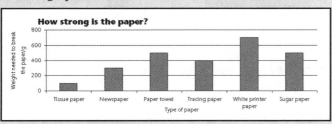

3. Most children will probably agree, saying it is because the tissue paper is thin and easy to tear.
4. Tissue paper.
5. Several answers are possible. Most children would say the sugar paper if they are shown a sample of it, because it is the thickest (though it actually has softer fibres that break more easily). You could use this opportunity to extend the discussion to how important appearance is for making predictions.
6. White printer paper.
7. The length and width of paper, type of mass, position of mass, distance between desks and place where the paper is taped to the desk are all possible. The amount of mass is not a correct answer, because that is what they are changing to find the strength.
8. Paper towel.
9. Use a selection of smaller masses as well (say, increase mass by 50g at a time).

How strong is the paper?

James and Raoul were investigating how strong different types of paper were. They cut a strip 20cm long and 2cm wide from each type of paper, and used sticky tape to stick the paper between two desks that were 16cm apart.

They tested the paper's strength by hanging 100g masses from the middle of each strip. Their teacher helped, so the masses didn't fall on anyone's toes.

Before starting, they predicted which type of paper would be the strongest.

Paper	Prediction (strongest =1)
Tissue paper	6
Newspaper	4
Paper towel	5
Tracing paper	2
White printer paper	3
Sugar paper	1

As they carried out the investigation they recorded their results in a table.

Paper	Mass needed to break the paper/g
Tissue paper	100
Newspaper	300
Paper towel	500
Tracing paper	400
White printer paper	700
Sugar paper	500

Questions

1. Draw a diagram of what you think the investigation would look like.

2. Draw a bar graph of the results. Don't forget to label the axes!

3. James and Raoul predicted that the tissue paper would be the weakest. Would you have predicted this as well? Explain why you agree or disagree.

4. Which type of paper was the weakest in the investigation?

5. James and Raoul predicted that the sugar paper would be the strongest – would you have predicted this as well? Explain why you agree or disagree.

6. Which paper was the strongest?

7. The children tried to make the investigation as fair as possible. Name two things they should have kept the same.

8. Which paper had the same strength as the sugar paper in this test?

9. How could you use different masses to find out whether these two papers had **exactly** the same strength?

HANDLING SCIENCE DATA YEAR 3

PERMEABLE ROCKS

National Curriculum Science KS2 PoS Sc3: 1d
QCA Science Unit 3D: Rocks and soils
Scottish 5–14 Guidelines Earth and space: Materials from Earth – Levels B, D

HOW TO GATHER THE DATA

This is a good opportunity to teach children to take care when investigating, that they will not always get the results they expect, and to use evidence to support new ideas. Children would probably not think that rocks soak up water, because they are solid and hard – but the evidence from this investigation supports the idea that they are permeable. You will need a balance to do the weighing (a balance that reads to the nearest 0.1g rather than 1g is better as it is more accurate, allowing you to use smaller samples of rock). If children are not confident with decimals, they could ignore numbers after the decimal point and just focus on whole numbers. It is probably easier if these children ignore the units as well, looking only at the numbers in order to highlight the trends. Note that chalk absorbs a lot of water, so needs to be allowed to dry thoroughly (or replaced) between investigations.

THE SCIENCE BEHIND THE DATA

There are three main types of rock: igneous (such as granite), sedimentary (such as sandstone) and metamorphic (such as slate).

Igneous rocks are formed from the molten material (magma) deep inside the Earth. Igneous rocks are very hard and not porous. They tend to look 'glassy' or have glassy, shiny particles in them. Sedimentary rocks are porous and permeable, formed by layers of sediment (sand or mud) sinking to the bottom of water and becoming compressed as more layers build up on top, cementing them together. Metamorphic rocks are sedimentary rocks that have been subjected to high temperatures and pressures under the surface of the Earth, so they have changed their structure.

You will need to introduce the idea of permeability to the children so they can answer questions 7 and 8. A permeable rock is one that will absorb water. It does this by letting water into the spaces between the particles in the rock. This can be modelled using a piece of sponge, showing that sponges become heavier when wet. Within the children's experience and reasoning, this idea can be applied to a new context (such as the activity shown opposite), thus widening their experience.

Answers

1. The air was coming out of the rock.
2. 7g, 0g, 1g , 1g, 18g
3. To remove any water that was on the outside of the rock that would affect their results and make the comparison less accurate.
4. Chalk.
5. Chalk.
6. Yes. Because the air is coming out of the rock and water is going in to replace it, the rock gets heavier.
7. 'Permeable' means that water can get in, or that the rock soaks up water.
8.

Name of rock	
Chalk	Most permeable
Sandstone	
Limestone	
Slate	
Granite	Least permeable

Permeable rocks

Julie and Jenny noticed that when some rocks were put in water, they could see bubbles coming out.

Julie thought the bubbles might be air coming from inside the rock. Jenny said the bubbles were just on the surface. They decided to investigate whether other rocks would do the same thing if they put them in water.

Their friend Jamila suggested they should weigh the rocks as well. "Weigh them at the start and at the end," she said, "and see if there is a difference."

They set up their investigation and tested five different rocks. Here are their results.

Rock	Mass before/g	Mass after/g	Change in mass/g	Bubbles?
Sandstone	45	52		Yes
Granite	42	42		No
Slate	48	49		Hardly any
Limestone	46	47		Only a few
Chalk	47	65		Lots

Questions

1. Why do you think Julie and Jenny could see bubbles coming from the rocks? Do you agree with either of them, or is there a different reason?

2. Work out the change in mass for each of the rocks they investigated.

3. After the rock had been in the water, they wiped it with a paper towel. Why do you think they did this?

4. Which rock gained the most mass?

5. Looking at the results, which rock do you think gave the most bubbles?

6. Do you think this provides evidence for Julie's explanation? Why?

7. Find out what the word 'permeable' means when we talk about rocks.

8. Write out the names of the rocks the children used, starting with the most permeable and finishing with the least.

Name of rock	
	Most permeable
	↑
	↓
	Least permeable

HANDLING SCIENCE DATA YEAR 3

SOIL SAMPLING

National Curriculum Science KS2 PoS Sc3: 1d
QCA Science Unit 3D: Rocks and soils
Scottish 5–14 Guidelines Earth and space: Materials from Earth – Levels B, D

HOW TO GATHER THE DATA

This is a good activity for children to carry out, but you will need to make your own mixtures of soil (you can buy different, ready-made soil samples from educational suppliers). From a health and safety point of view, if you do make your own samples, it is best to use sterile compost, clean sand and powdered clay; by using different amounts you can alter the water retention of the mixture. More sand reduces water retention, while more clay increases water retention.

It helps to drop a small stone or put metal gauze into the funnel to stop the soil coming through when carrying out the investigation. You'll also need to ensure that the children are familiar with the use of cubic centimetres (cm³) as a unit of volume.

THE SCIENCE BEHIND THE DATA

Soil is a mixture of stones, sand, silt, clay and humus, which all retain water in varying degrees. Stones retain virtually no water – the surface gets wet, but nearly all of the water simply runs off. Some water does get trapped in the gaps between grains of sand, so it will retain some water, but most will drain through. Silt is very fine sand, so it will hold on to more water.

Clay can hold onto large amounts of water. It consists of layers of charged particles (ions), and when it gets wet the structure opens up and retains water particles between the layers. Clay soil gets very waterlogged.

Humus is the rotting remains of dead animals and plants. Because it contains a lot of cellulose material and is very porous, it is good for holding onto water. Humus is better for plants than clay because it holds the water in the material but allows air around it, so it doesn't get waterlogged.

If the children are confident with the idea of the water passing the pebbles in Question 9, you can extend this idea to the concept that this is how all the samples let water though: it trickles through the spaces between the particles of stone, sand, silt and so on. This allows you to bring in the idea that water, as a liquid, can change its shape and so get past the solid particles.

Answers

1.

Group name	Volume of water/cm³
Alison's group	50
Bert's group	20
Chris's group	60
Dave's group	40
Eddie's group	60

2. A bar to the height of 60cm³.
3. Eddie's group.
4. 50cm³.
5. Bert's group.
6. The one that holds on to the most water will let the least water through: 20cm³, Bert's group.
7. Several answers are possible: the same amount of soil (you might prefer scoops, mass or volume); the same time for it to drip through or until it stops dripping. Children might suggest using the same measuring cylinder, but this is not a fair test consideration as cm³ are the same on any measuring cylinder. You may or may not want to deal with this now, depending on whether you think the children will understand this. Some children may also say using the same type of soil – you will need to deal with this because the soil should be changed in each group to compare different ones.
8. An amount close to 100cm³.
9. The water can flow through the gaps and past the stones, so none of it gets trapped.

Soil sampling

Class 3 had read that plants need water in order to live and grow, so they decided to test some soil samples to see how much water they would soak up.

Groups of children each put some soil in a funnel and measured 100cm³ of water in a jug to pour onto each sample of soil. Then they waited until no more water dripped out into the measuring cylinder underneath.

This is a diagram of the class's results.

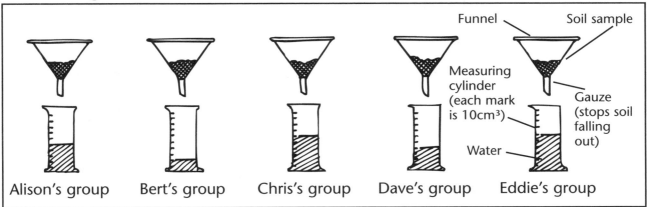

Alison's group   Bert's group   Chris's group   Dave's group   Eddie's group

Questions

1. Complete this table by taking the results from the diagram above.

Group name	Volume of water/cm³

2. This is a graph of their results.

Complete the graph by drawing in Eddie's group's result.

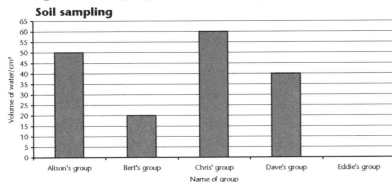

3. Which sample let the most water through?

4. How much water came through in Alison's group's experiment?

5. Which group's soil held onto the most water? Think carefully!

6. Explain how you found the answer to question 5.

7. Name two things each group should keep the same to make it a fair test.

8. Another group, Freda's group, tried the investigation with some small pebbles. How much water do you think would come through to their measuring cylinder?

9. Explain your answer to Question 8.

HANDLING SCIENCE DATA YEAR 3

SIEVING SOIL

National Curriculum Science KS2 PoS Sc3: 1a
QCA Science Unit 3D: Rocks and soils.
Scottish 5–14 Guidelines Earth and space: Changing materials –
Level C

HOW TO GATHER THE DATA

This activity works better if you make your own mixtures of soils. From a health and safety point of view, it is better to use washed stones, sterile compost, clean sand and powdered clay, or you can buy different, ready-made soil samples from science educational suppliers – even if you buy these, it would be a good idea to put some small stones in as well. You can alter the proportions of different components according to the sieves you have available.

It's important that your sample of material is very dry, so that the children can sieve the materials easily. For your own sanity, have plenty of newspaper available and carry out the investigation in an area that is easily cleaned!

THE SCIENCE BEHIND THE DATA

Soil is a mixture of stones, sand, silt, clay and humus. All of these will, in varying quantities, pass through sieves. In order of decreasing size, they are:
Stones: some larger ones will be trapped by most sieves.
Humus: this is the rotting remains of dead animals and plants. It will vary a lot in size (a stick may get trapped passing through a sieve in one direction but not the other), and this can be used with the children to discuss how they should carry out their investigation.
Sand: grains of sand will pass through quite a small sieve, so the coarser it is the better. Grit will probably be useful.
Silt and clay: both are very fine, so they will go through all the sieves you are likely to have in the classroom.

Using knowledge of these properties, you can experiment with different components on their own, or you can mix different soils, or both.

When children are describing or explaining the effect of sieves, they have a tendency to use phrases like 'the stones are big', or 'the holes are small'. Try and develop these simple statements so that the children always make a comparison between the size of the particles and the size of the holes (for example, 'the stones do not go through the first sieve because they are bigger than the holes', or 'the sand goes through because it is smaller than the holes'). This activity is ideal for developing precision in children's use of language, which is essential if they are going to be able to explain their developing ideas and concepts fully and clearly at a later stage.

Answers

1.

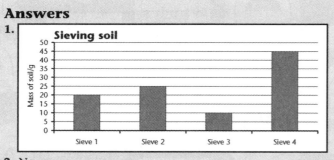

2. No.
3. They still had 100g of soil if you add the masses of soil in all four sieves.
4. 90g
5. You start with twice as much soil, so you should get twice as much in each sieve (if the soil is identical).
6. The soil particles go through the first sieve if they are smaller than the holes, but if they are bigger than the holes in the second sieve they will not go through it.
7a. So the soil will not all stick together. **b.** The amount of moisture in different kinds of soil varies a lot, so it will affect the mass of the soil samples.

Sieving soil

Annie, Katy and Marie were trying out different sieves on some dry soil. Each sieve had different-sized holes.

■ They put 100g of soil in the sieve with the largest holes in it, and tapped the sieve until no more soil would go through.

■ They weighed the soil that was left in the first sieve using some scales.

■ Then they took all the soil that passed through the first sieve and put it in a second sieve, which had smaller holes in it.

■ They tapped this sieve until no more soil would go through, then weighed what was left in the second sieve.

■ They repeated this with a third and a fourth sieve, each with smaller holes than the last, so they ended up with four piles of soil that they weighed.

These are the results:

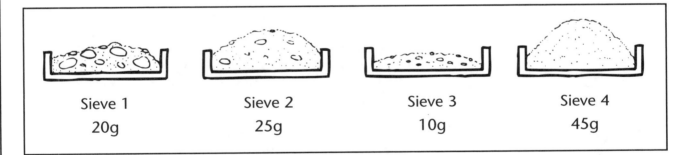

Sieve 1	Sieve 2	Sieve 3	Sieve 4
20g	25g	10g	45g

Questions

1. Plot the data from the girls' investigation as a graph.

2. Did they lose any of the soil they started with?

3. How did you work this out?

4. If they started with 200g of the same soil as before, how much would be left in the fourth sieve?

5. Explain how you worked this out.

6. Explain why some soil goes through the first sieve but not the second.

7. The children dried the soil before they sieved it. Give two possible reasons for doing this.

HANDLING SCIENCE DATA YEAR 3

STRETCHING TIGHTS

National Curriculum Science KS2 PoS Sc3: 1a
QCA Science Unit 3C: Characteristics of materials
Scottish 5–14 Guidelines Earth and space: Materials from Earth –
Levels A, B; Changing materials – Level A

HOW TO GATHER THE DATA

This is a fun investigation that provides a good opportunity for children to participate in making a human graph – details of which can be found in *Getting to Grips with Graphs* (A Goldsworthy, V Wood-Robinson and R Watson (1999, ASE). A story can be used effectively to stimulate this investigation:

> I live in the country and the nearest shops are 20 miles away. The village shop sells tights that fit me – a small person. My cousin came to stay yesterday. She is very, very tall. She forgot her tights and it's very cold. I offered to lend her some, but there is a problem... [show a pair of unstretched tights] I've brought in some of my tights, can you help me stretch them so she can use them?

The children will respond well to this investigation if brightly coloured tights are used – the more garish the better! Two medium-sized onions can be used instead of a 200g mass.

The children should extend both their vocabulary and their knowledge of materials in this activity, using words such as *strong, hard, soft, flexible, stretchy* and *elastic* to describe properties of materials – and finding out what these mean scientifically. They can relate the use of materials to their characteristics: why do tights need to be stretchy? What do we use elastic bands for? What sort of clothes is Lycra used for?

THE SCIENCE BEHIND THE DATA

Elasticity is the scientific term used to describe the 'stretchiness' of a material. A material is elastic if it returns to its original shape after stretching. Lycra, tights, elastic bands and other elastic materials are made from chemical substances called polymers – these contain chains of very large molecules. Stretching pulls against the forces holding the chains together; when the stretching force is removed, the forces in the material make it return to its original shape. In some cases of polymers, such as elastic bands, the chains are coiled up and stretching uncoils them; when the force is released the polymer coils up again.

Answers

1. A diagram showing a weighted leg longer than an unweighted leg and the difference between the two measured using a tape or metre ruler. ➤

2.

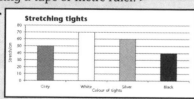

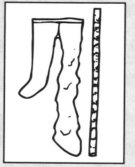

Any graph similar to this. The relative heights should match.
3. A metre ruler or tape measure.
4. The white ones.
5. 50cm.
6. The following are correct: the mass (200g), the length of the tights at the start, the points used for measuring (eg from one toe to the other) each time. Using the same ruler is not a fair test consideration, as centimetres are the same on any ruler.
7. To make the investigation fair.
8. The black tights may be thicker, or be more closely woven.
9. The white tights may be made of thinner material, or be more loosely woven and so stretchier.
10. Several answers are possible: elastic bands, springs, bubble gum, elastic items of clothing, Lycra T-shirts, sports clothing.
11. Look for several things: how to hang masses to stretch the samples, where to measure from and to, the sample size, whether you can use a force meter to measure the pull.

Stretching tights

A group of children carried out an investigation to find out which colour of tights was the stretchiest. They hung each pair up and added the same mass (200g) to one leg of each pair of tights. Then they measured the difference between the lengths of the leg with the mass in and the leg with no mass.

They recorded their results as a human graph, and later as a bar chart using the computer.

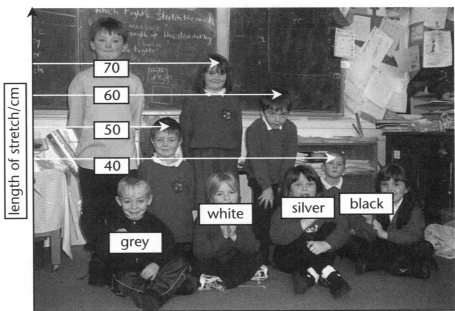

colour of tights

Questions

1. Draw a picture to show how the children could measure the stretchiness of these tights.

2. What do you think the children's computer graph will look like? Draw it on a sheet of graph paper, remembering to label your axes.

3. What piece of equipment could the children use to measure how far the tights stretched?

4. Which colour of tights stretched the most?

5. By how much did the grey tights stretch?

6. What things should the children keep the same for each measurement?

7. Why should they keep these things the same?

8. Can you think of a reason why the black tights are the least stretchy?

9. Why do you think the white tights are the most stretchy?

10. Name three other materials you can think of that are stretchy.

11. Describe how could you investigate the stretchiness of one of these other materials. Draw a diagram to go with your description.

y

PHOTOCOPIABLE ▲ SCHOLASTIC

BUBBLEGUM

National Curriculum Science KS2 PoS Sc3: 1a, 2b
QCA Science Unit 3C: Characteristics of materials
Scottish 5–14 Guidelines Earth and space: Materials from Earth –
Level A; Changing materials – Levels A, C

HOW TO GATHER THE DATA

This is undoubtedly an activity that children will find fascinating, and – believe it or not – it does give good results, though as a practical activity it may be better designed as an investigation of which child can blow the biggest bubble. The written activity shown opposite can be done as reinforcement of a practical activity, or as a brainstorm session where the children could plan a practical activity. There are clearly hygiene and safety issues that need to be addressed here, as well as those of everyday classroom management! As a practical assessment activity, this will be a good vehicle for the children to look at fair testing and the best way to make the measurements.

THE SCIENCE BEHIND THE DATA

Bubblegum is a 'plastic' material, not an elastic one: an elastic material returns to its original size and shape after being stretched, but a plastic one (like the actual material plastic) will remain stretched. These materials have long-chain molecules that can slide past each other and still have reasonably strong forces of attraction that hold the chains close to each other. Often it is water molecules that form a bridge between the chains: chewing the gum warms and lubricates the chains so that they flow past each other and the block of gum can change shape. You might like to discuss with the children whether gum is a solid or a liquid. (It is not a pure substance, but a mixture of a solid and a liquid, and so does not fall into either category.)

This activity also addresses the use of forces: the harder you blow, the bigger the bubble. The air particles are forced out of the person's lungs and collide with the walls of the bubble, which creates the pressure inside the bubble. This has to be within limits, though, because you need to allow time for the chains of molecules in the gum to flow past each other as the bubble expands. Blowing too quickly will cause the bubble to rupture at its weakest point.

Measuring the bubbles is tricky; probably the easiest way is to span the bubble with your fingers and then measure the gap with a ruler. Alternatively, you can hold a ruler next to the bubble and estimate its width by eye, although this may lead children to question the accuracy of the results.

Answers

1. Several answers may be suggested by the children; judge them according to the children's reasoning. You could ask the children to discuss how their ideas would affect the results. Possible answers are: the amount of gum used, the time to chew, the number of chews, the strength of chewing action, the amount of saliva, the temperature of the gum beforehand (is it kept in a pocket?), the hardness/softness of gum at the start, how hard the bubble was blown.

2. You can allow the children to measure in centimetres or millimetres.

Brand of gum	Size of bubble/mm
Yummy Bubby	65
Bubbly Dubbly	50
Gum Yum	30
Supa Doopa	75
Hubby Wubby	40

3. The bar chart should match the results table.

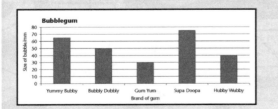

Bubblegum

Year 3 were having a competition to see who could blow the biggest bubble from some different brands of bubblegum. The children could choose their favourite gum to bring in, and they were going to see which brand was the best.

All the children's bubbles are shown below.

Questions

1. Can you name three things that the children must agree on to make their investigation fair?

2. Measure all the bubbles on the page using a ruler and then make a table of the results.

3. Plot the results as a bar graph.

PETER'S PROBLEM

National Curriculum Science KS2 PoS Sc3: 2a; Sc4: 2d, 2e
QCA Science Unit 3C: Characteristics of materials; 3E: Magnets and springs
Scottish 5–14 Guidelines Earth and space: Materials from Earth – Level B; Energy and forces: Forces and their effects – Level B

HOW TO GATHER THE DATA

This is an activity that Year 3 children will enjoy doing, and it is well within their capabilities if they do it carefully. It is very good for developing skills such as lining up accurately, reading scales and using the zero mark on a ruler, as the concepts are set inside the children's everyday experiences. The children can easily tell whether they are performing the activity accurately, can understand the effect that inaccuracies will have on their results, and will know if they have results that need to be checked.

For this investigation the pulling force needs to be within the elasticity of the material. If you keep using a bigger force, you won't get a linear pattern because the material behaves differently (see below).

THE SCIENCE BEHIND THE DATA

'Elasticity' is the scientific term used to describe the stretchiness of materials. A material is elastic if it returns to its original shape after stretching. In an elastic band, the particles of plastic (they're not made of rubber any more) are arranged in long chains that are all coiled up. If you stretch an elastic band, the chains of molecules uncoil and form a straighter line. Eventually these chains are pulled straight; it will then take a much bigger pulling force to overcome the forces holding the chains together. If this happens, you break the chains apart and the elastic snaps. As the band stretches, its length increases in proportion with the force applied, until the chains are fully stretched.

Note that in the activity shown opposite, the force needed to stretch the elastic band to a particular length is used to measure 'how hard' the elastic band is to pull. This is a logical step because the more force the child exerts in stretching the band, the more effort his or her muscles will need to make. The force used to stretch the band is equal to the pulling force exerted by the band in the opposite direction.

Answers

1. 14cm
2. 5N (or the largest force)
3. A bar equivalent to 23cm length of elastic.
4. The bigger the force, the longer the elastic (see the 'Springy science' activity on page 56 for how to help the children with this).
5. The elastic has a 5cm length before you start stretching it.
6. A table such as this:

Pull from force meter/N	Length of elastic/cm
0	5
1	8
2	11
3	14
4	17
5	20

7. 11cm.
8. 17cm (stretch at 2N = 6cm; stretch at 4N = 12cm).
9. They would need a bigger force to give the same amount of stretch.

Peter's problem

Miss Brown's class were looking at materials. Peter found some elastic bands.
   "Miss," he said, "when you stretch an elastic band more, it's harder to pull."
   "When is it twice as hard to pull?" said Miss Brown.
   "I don't know," said Peter.
   "Well, go and find out," she replied. "You'll need this force meter." Peter went back to his table and asked his friend Joyce to help him.

This diagram shows how they decided to do the investigation.

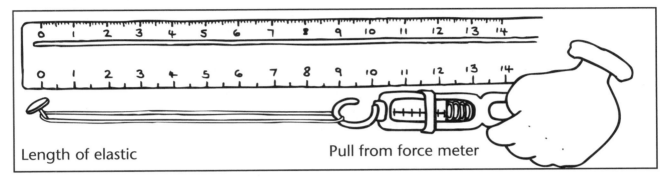

Length of elastic   Pull from force meter

They plotted their results as a bar graph:

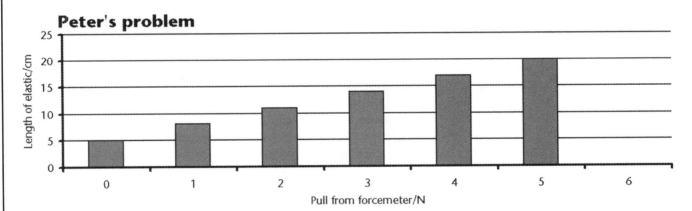

Questions

1. What was the length of the elastic band when stretched by a force of 3N?

2. Which pull gave the longest stretch?

3. Draw a bar on the graph to show the length of the elastic for a pull of 6N.

4. Describe how the length of the elastic varies with the amount of pull.

5. Why does the graph not go down to zero when there is no force applied?

6. Use the graph to read the results and write them in a table.

7. What was the length of the band when the force applied was 2N?

8. How long was the band when the force was twice as much as that?

9. If Peter and Joyce used a thicker elastic band, how do you think this would affect their results?

THE SOLAR SYSTEM

National Curriculum Science KS2 PoS Sc3: 2c
QCA Science Unit 3F: Light and shadows
Scottish 5–14 Guidelines Earth and space: Earth in space – Level C

HOW TO GATHER THE DATA

Looking at the planets is a good opportunity for children to use CD-ROMs and Internet searches: different groups can research different topics or different planets. Children do not need to gather a lot of factual information on this theme in terms of National Curriculum coverage in England, but topics on 'space' invariably interest them and can be used to develop presentation skills and as information in the context of other curriculum areas.

While the magnitude of the numbers involved in space data may not be familiar to the children, don't let this put you off – there is much that they can gain from looking at the planets. In this activity, the emphasis is on looking at the size of the bars on the graph relative to one another, rather than dealing with the numbers they represent.

THE SCIENCE BEHIND THE DATA

Children do not need to know any information about planets for the National Curriculum in England, but the Scottish 5–14 Guidelines require children to be able to describe the Solar System and link the temperatures of the planets to their relative positions and the presence of an atmosphere. A useful mnemonic to put the planets in the correct order is 'My Very Easy Method Just Speeds Up Naming Planets'.

The further away from the Sun the planets are, the colder they are. The intensity of the Sun's radiation decreases the further away you are. This means that a graph of temperature will decrease (as a curve) with distance. Note, however, that the graph is not to the scale of distance: it simply ranks the planets in order of distance from the Sun.

The temperatures in this activity are measured in kelvin, which is known as an 'absolute' temperature scale (you do not write °K, just K as a unit). 0K is known as 'absolute zero' (equivalent to –273°C), and no temperature can be lower than this.

The other major factor in determining the surface temperature of a planet is the nature of its atmosphere. Mercury, Mars and Pluto all have much thinner atmospheres than Earth, because gravity is not strong enough on these planets to hold onto gases that instead drift off into space. The presence of an atmosphere will increase the temperature because the gases absorb high-energy radiation (light) and emit lower-energy radiation (heat) – this is the same effect as global warming due to the greenhouse effect. 'Greenhouse' gases such as carbon dioxide and methane do this to a great effect, so cause a higher temperature than would otherwise exist. It's worth remembering that without this natural level of greenhouse effect, we could not survive on our planet.

Answers

1. Venus.
2. Pluto.
3. The children may say that Mercury should be hotter (which is the 'correct' theory – it has too little atmosphere to keep the planet warmed up), but they may choose Venus because it is higher than Mercury (otherwise, the temperature decreases with distance from the Sun). From the children's point of view, both answers are acceptable.
4. The children should give a rational explanation related to the general curved pattern of the graph.
5. Venus is nearer to the Sun.
6. A bar whose height is between those of Jupiter and Uranus.
7. A value between 60K and 125K (the actual value is 95K).
8. Mars: 250K.
9. Venus has a higher temperature than Mercury because it has an atmosphere (containing 97% carbon dioxide) and Mercury does not.

The Solar System

Henry and Matt looked on the Internet to find some data about the planets. They found the temperatures of the planets using a scale of temperature called kelvin (the unit is K).

They have plotted the data as a bar graph.

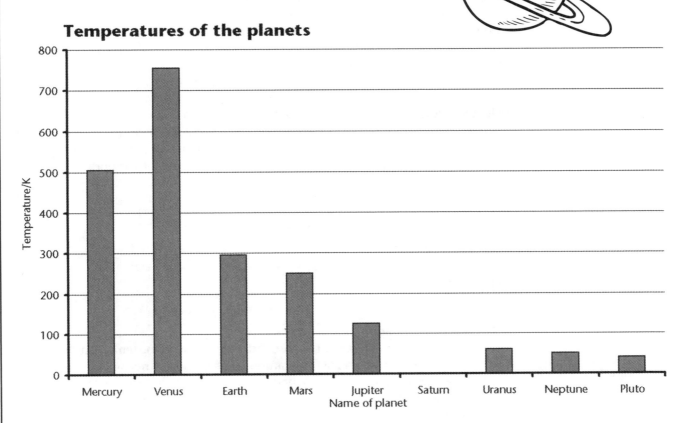

Temperatures of the planets

They forgot to plot the temperature for Saturn!

Questions

1. Which planet is the hottest?
2. Which planet is the coldest?
3. Which planet does not seem to fit a regular pattern?
4. Why did you choose that planet?
5. Can you explain why Venus is hotter than the Earth?
6. Draw a bar to show how hot Saturn is on the graph.
7. What temperature do you think it has?
8. Which planet has a temperature twice as high as that of Jupiter?
9. Find out why the temperature of Venus is higher than that of Mercury.

WARM WEATHER

National Curriculum Science KS2 PoS Sc3: 2c
QCA Science Unit 3F: Light and shadows
Scottish 5–14 Guidelines Energy and forces: Properties and uses of energy – Level B; Earth and space: Changing materials – Level B

HOW TO GATHER THE DATA

Any type of weather reports can be used to gather this information, which is available from newspapers, television or many websites (look at www.metoffice.gov.uk for comprehensive information).

THE SCIENCE BEHIND THE DATA

The temperature of the Earth depends upon the energy transferred from the Sun, so it is hotter during the day when the Sun is shining on us than at night when it isn't. The Sun shines more directly on the equator than on the northern and southern hemispheres, where it shines at an angle due to the Earth's tilt (you can model this with a torch: when the torch is directly above the desk the light is brighter and less spread out than when you hold the torch at an angle to the desk). This means that the radiation from the Sun will be most intense at the equator, and the temperature will be hottest. Average temperatures decrease the further away from the equator you go, so northern Scotland will have lower average temperatures than Southern England. The effect is not, as some children may think, due to any significant difference in distance from the Sun – the Sun is 150 million kilometres (93 million miles) away!

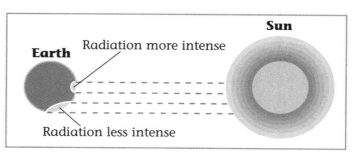

Answers

1. London.
2. Inverness.
3. 13°C
4. Liverpool.
5. Answer appropriate to the city chosen.
6. The cities that are further south are warmer. The temperature increases the further south (or the nearer the equator) you go.
7. Cardiff.
8. London.
9. The sunlight shines directly on us during the day, but not at night.

Warm weather

Temperatures at midday

Here is a map showing the temperatures at midday in different parts of Britain.

Temperatures at midnight

Here the map is showing the temperatures at midnight in the same parts of Britain.

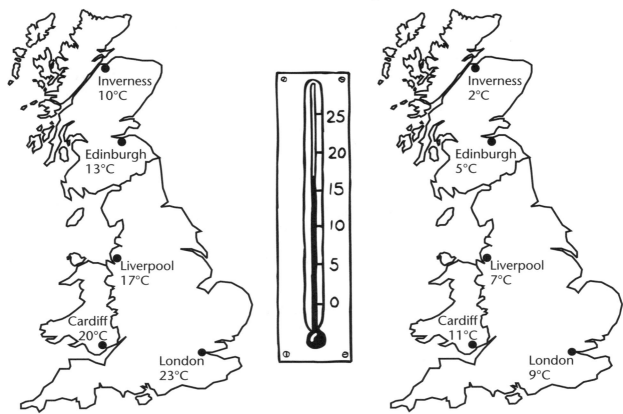

Questions

1. Which place has the highest temperature at midday?

2. Which place has the lowest temperature at midday?

3. What is the difference in temperature between London and Inverness at midday?

4. Which city's temperature is shown on the thermometer?

5. Mark and label the midday temperature of one other city on the thermometer on the right.

6. Why are the temperatures higher in some parts of the country than in others?

7. Which city has the highest temperature at midnight?

8. Which city experienced the largest drop in temperature between midday and midnight?

9. Why are the temperatures higher during the day than at night?

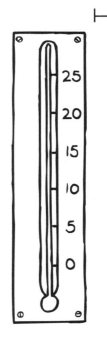

HANDLING SCIENCE DATA YEAR 3

MUFFLING MATERIALS

> **National Curriculum Science** KS2 PoS Sc3: 1a
> **QCA Science** Unit 3C: Characteristics of materials
> **Scottish 5–14 Guidelines** Earth and space: Materials from
> Earth – Levels A, B

HOW TO GATHER THE DATA

There are some practical difficulties to overcome if you are conducting this investigation yourself. The main problem is that sound travels better through solids than through gases, so any solid material touching the sound sensor will have an effect like tapping on a microphone: the sound will be louder. If you keep the material quite loose and don't put the source and sensor on the same surface, you can get satisfactory results that fit the expected pattern.

When carrying out any datalogging activity, it's important not to be overwhelmed by the numbers and results the children may obtain – in many cases, children can understand and compare percentage values from a datalogger by thinking of them as numbers to 100 on a number line. Similarly, children may well be able to read these values off a computer-plotted graph such as the one on this worksheet, and be able to look at the heights of the bars and compare them.

THE SCIENCE BEHIND THE DATA

Sound travels in waves that vibrate the particles of a medium like ripples in a pond (whether this is a solid, a liquid or a gas). It travels from one point to another as the vibrations pass through the medium. Sound cannot pass through a vacuum (secondary schools often have equipment to demonstrate this), because there are no particles in a vacuum to transmit vibrations.

A solid is the best medium for sound to travel through; a gas is the worst. In a solid, the sound travels faster and you can hear a louder sound because the particles in a solid are very close together and the vibrations

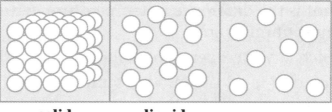

solid   **liquid**   **gas**

can pass easily from one particle to the next. In a gas the particles are far apart, so it is much more difficult to pass the vibrations on. When you are trying to muffle sound, a material that traps air inside (such as cotton wool) works best as the sound will travel least well through and between the air pockets in the material.

Answers

1. Aluminum foil (93dB).
2. Cotton wool (62dB).
3. Paper and silk (85dB).
4. Woolly cloth.
5. Cotton wool.
6. It lets the least sound through.
7. The cotton wool traps air inside, blocking the sound vibrations that the air carries. The vibrating air gets trapped in the little pockets, so the sound does not pass through the material effectively. The children might say 'because it is thicker', which is a correct statement – but try to encourage them to explain in more detail if possible.
8. Several answers are possible: the sound source, the sound level, the distance, the amount of material, the method of wrapping.
9.

Material	Muffling ability
Cotton wool	Best
Woolly cloth	
Curtain	
Silk/paper	
Paper/silk	
Aluminium foil	Poorest

Muffling materials

Have you ever noticed that if you cover your ears, sounds are harder to hear? Your hands block out the sound. Some Year 3 children were testing materials to see how well they muffled sound. They wrapped different materials around a sound probe connected to a datalogger, as shown below.

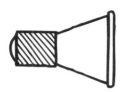

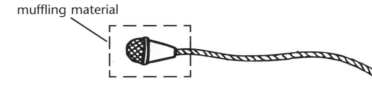

muffling material

The children plotted a graph of their results.

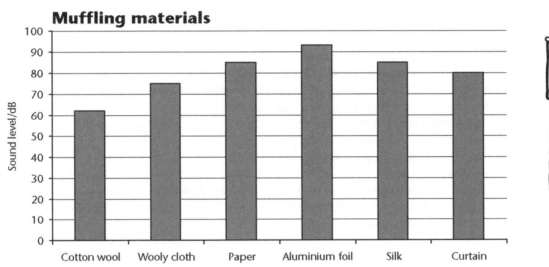

75dB

Questions

1. Which material gave the highest sound level?

2. Which material gave the lowest sound level?

3. Which two materials gave the same reading?

4. Look at the datalogger in the picture. Which material is being tested?

5. Which material is best at muffling sounds?

6. How did you decide this?

7. Can you explain why this material is best at muffling sounds?

8. Name three things the children should keep the same to make the investigation a fair test.

9. Fill in the table to put the materials in order of muffling ability, the best first.

Material	Muffling ability
	Best
	↑
	↓
	Poorest

HANDLING SCIENCE DATA YEAR 3

INVESTIGATING DIFFERENT SURFACES

National Curriculum Science KS2 PoS Sc3: 1a
QCA Science Unit 3C: Characteristics of materials
Scottish 5–14 Guidelines Earth and space: Materials from Earth – Level B

HOW TO GATHER THE DATA

It is easy to set up this investigation with groups of children. It's important to position the boards so the ends overlap with the edge of the desk, as shown on the worksheet. You could use plastic margarine tubs and 10g and 100g masses to pull the block across the surfaces. Expect to use larger masses to move the block on the carpet (remember 500g is quite a large mass, so the children need to take care not to drop them on toes or fingers).

Show the children examples of the different surfaces, allowing them to feel each surface. Use magnifying glasses so the children can examine the surfaces more closely and confirm their observations. Ask the children to predict which of the surfaces the block will slide across most easily before they carry out the investigation.

The investigation could also be carried out by using force meters to pull the objects across the surfaces. (This is effectively what the masses inside the margarine tub are used to measure – the latter will be useful if your school has a small number of force meters available. Remember that 100g provides a force of approximately 1N.)

Ask the children to observe what happens when the block starts to move. It will suddenly start moving, rather than sliding gradually. This is because it takes more force to start an object moving than to keep it moving.

THE SCIENCE BEHIND THE DATA

Year 3 children may or may not have come across friction as a phenomenon, so you need to decide on the appropriate vocabulary for them. The children should observe that the greatest force is needed to start the block moving (against static friction), but that once the block starts moving, it moves quickly (against dynamic friction, which is a lesser force).

The wooden and plastic surfaces are very smooth, so there is very little friction between the block and the surface. The tile in this experiment is a ceramic tile; it is hard and smooth, so again there is little friction. The carpet, though, is rough, hairy, bumpy, fluffy – the friction between the carpet and the block is comparatively large (requiring 500g – a pull of approximately 5N – to move the block). The children can use a mixture of their own vocabulary (which can be very expressive) and new words learned in science.

Calculating averages is not a Year 3 task, but it is good practice to repeat measurements in an investigation to ensure reliability, and the children can appreciate the reasons for doing so at this stage in their development.

Answers
1. 300g
2. 70g
3. 230g
4. Because they knew there could be errors, and by repeating the measurements and taking the average they would get a more reliable result.
5. Discuss the reasons with the children: perhaps slightly different positioning of the block on the starting line, or the masses in the tub.
6. Mass of wooden block, the tub, distance between the start and finishing lines, length of the string.
7. The carpet is the roughest surface (the most friction).
8. The wooden surface was the smoothest (the least friction).
9. Easier. The oil is slippy, so it will reduce the friction even more.
10. Link the material to the justification: tile or plastic because it is waterproof; or carpet because water will make the others even slippier. Both are valid answers if justified.

Investigating different surfaces

Class 3 had a slippy surface by the door of their classroom. They wanted to find a safer one for walking on, so they set up an investigation.

They tested boards covered with different materials: wood, smooth plastic, carpet and tile. They marked out start and finish lines, 40cm apart, and placed a wooden block on one of the surfaces at the start line. This was connected to a tub using string. They put masses in the tub until the block moved over the finish line.

Surface	Average mass to move block/g 1st try	2nd try	Average mass to move block/g
Carpet	280	320	300
Plastic	90	110	100
Tile	70	70	70
Wood	60	60	60

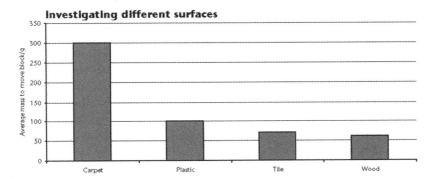

They tested each surface twice, and worked out the average weight needed to make the block move from start to finish. They plotted a graph of their results.

Questions

1. How much mass was needed to move the wooden block across the carpet?

2. How much mass was needed to move the wooden block across the tile?

3. What is the difference between the masses needed to pull the block across the carpet and across the tile?

4. Why did the children repeat the measurements?

5. Why do you think some of the measurements the children made were slightly different between the first and second tries?

6. What things did the children need to keep the same in their investigation?

7. Why was the largest mass required to move the block on the carpet?

8. Why did the wooden surface require the smallest mass to move the block?

9. If you coated the wooden board with oil, would it be easier or harder to move the block? Why do you think this?

10. Which do you think would be the best material to use near a sink? Why?

HANDLING SCIENCE DATA YEAR 3

REFLECTING LIGHT

National Curriculum Science KS2 PoS Sc3: 1a; Sc4: 3c
QCA Science Unit 3F: Light and shadows
Scottish 5–14 Guidelines Earth and space: materials from Earth –
Level A, B; Energy and forces: properties and uses of energy – Level C

HOW TO GATHER THE DATA

There are several ways of obtaining data for this type of graph. Children can direct a ray of light from a torch (through a slit cut from black paper placed across the torch) onto a surface and measure the reflected light using a light sensor attached to a datalogger. It is better to do this in a shaded room.

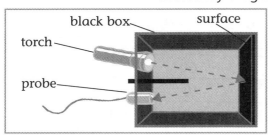

Alternatively, a light source such as a torch can be shone onto the back of a black box (where the surface to be tested is placed) and a light probe adjacent to the torch (but separated from it by a black partition) can detect the reflected light. (See diagram on left.)

Any data-logging activity is likely to throw up numbers that the children are not familiar with. It's important not to be scared of dealing with these numbers and to realise that, even though children aren't necessarily familiar with percentages, they will be able to interpret the data readings relative to one another, and will be able to understand readings in terms of their position on a number line.

THE SCIENCE BEHIND THE DATA

The fact that we see an object because light from a source reflects off the object and into our eyes is a very difficult concept for most children (and many adults!) to grasp. In a totally dark room, we cannot see at all because there is no light being reflected into our eyes. Many schools have a stock cupboard that can be used to demonstrate this – which can be quite an eerie experience for adults, let alone children. It is, though, well worth the effort of setting up this experience.

Children need to explore the amount of light reflected from different surfaces to extend their thinking about light. With no light, even a shiny surface cannot be seen (children are very likely to predict that they will be able to see a shiny surface in a completely black room). If a small amount of light is introduced into a dark room or a black box, mirrors or silver surfaces are always the first things to be seen because they reflect the most light into our eyes. In contrast, black objects are very difficult to see as they reflect very little light. All these activities emphasise the idea of seeing by reflected light.

Answers

1. 1
2. The mirror.
3. 2
4. Black.
5. Dull. (It is useful if the children can use all the words that describe the effects of light on different materials in the correct contexts.)
6. 4
7. White.
8.

Surface	Light reflected/%
1	99
2	5
3	58
4	83

9. About 20%. (The number should be nearer to the black value than the yellow value.)
10. The white clothes reflect a lot of light (for example, from a car's headlamps), so drivers can see us more clearly.
11. Fluorescent.

Reflecting light

Ira and Esi used a light probe attached to a datalogger to measure the reflection of light from different surfaces. The computer stored the data and created a bar graph, but they forgot to write down the order in which they tested the surfaces.

They can remember the four surfaces they used: a mirror, white card, yellow card and black card.

This is the graph the computer produced.

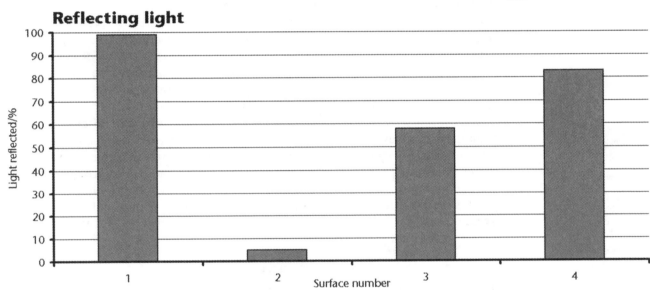

Questions

1. Which surface reflected the most light: 1, 2, 3 or 4?

2. Which of the four materials do you think will reflect this amount of light?

3. Which surface reflected the least light: 1, 2, 3 or 4?

4. What colour do you think this surface is?

5. What word is used to describe surfaces that are poor reflectors of light?

6. Which surface reflected 83% of the light: 1, 2, 3 or 4?

7. What colour do you think this surface is?

8. Design and fill in a table that Ira and Esi could use to record their results.

9. Can you predict roughly how much light a brown surface will reflect?

10. Why should we wear white if we walk down a dark road at night?

11. Find out the word that describes special safety clothing that stands out at night.

SEE-THROUGH OR NOT?

National Curriculum Science KS2 PoS Sc4: 3b
QCA Science Unit 3F: Light and shadows
Scottish 5–14 Guidelines Energy and forces: Properties and uses of energy – Level B/C

HOW TO GATHER THE DATA

This investigation requires the use of some sort of light meter or datalogger. Samples of fabric can be cut up into small squares with different sets for each group – or, if equipment is scarce, you may have to carry this out in conjunction with other activities while each group does the data-logging activity. Alternatively, carry the investigation out as a whole-class activity with the children trying to arrange the materials in a 'rank order'.

It can help to promote discussion of results if the children have predicted what the readings will be before carrying out this experiment. They could try to decide whether each material should be classified as transparent, translucent or opaque. For a good discussion, try to find dark cellophane (available from educational suppliers or craft shops) that gives a lower reading than tracing paper – this clarifies the definition of 'translucent'.

Most adults, let alone children, will rank the tracing paper after the cellophane samples. This comparison can be used to move away from the general – but not quite correct – idea that 'translucent' means 'some light comes through': a sort of midway position that's not opaque, but not quite transparent. Translucent materials let light through, but without letting you see the detail of the image that is behind it: you can see bright lights and shadows, but you cannot see the object clearly because the light is scattered more than through a transparent material such as cellophane.

THE SCIENCE BEHIND THE DATA

Transparent materials let light through, allowing you to see a clear image and the detail of what you are looking at. Translucent materials let light through, but scatter it so that you cannot see the details of what you are looking at. Opaque materials do not let light through.

The materials used in this investigation have been deliberately chosen to highlight the differences between these definitions, which are not as clear-cut as is often suggested. Only the black paper is truly opaque, letting no light through. The paper towel at first glance appears opaque, but on closer inspection (possibly after a datalogger reading) the children will find it does let some light through.

So what qualifies as 'opaque'? Is it only something that gives a zero reading? If this is the case, a lot of materials that we might think are opaque are not actually so. For everyday purposes, we might have a 'working idea' of opaque that includes materials that allow a small amount of light to come through. Similarly, you might be able to use polythene to promote a discussion about when 'transparent' becomes 'translucent'. As you increase the thickness of the polythene you are looking through, it becomes more difficult to make out a clear image. This can illustrate to the children that there is not always a 'correct' answer: sometimes they (and all other scientists) have to make a subjective judgement.

Answers

1. Use the same thickness of paper and the same light source.
2. Colourless cellophane.
3. The black paper. This had the lowest amount of light passing through.
4. Tracing paper.
5.

Type of paper	Light passed/%
Colourless cellophane	99
Yellow cellophane	88
Tracing paper	75
Purple cellophane	72
Paper towel	34
Black paper	0

See-through or not?

Some children were using a datalogger to measure how much light would pass through six different samples of paper.

They put a piece of paper over the light sensor and took a reading from the datalogger. If nothing was covering the light sensor, the light reading was 100%.

The children made a graph of their results:

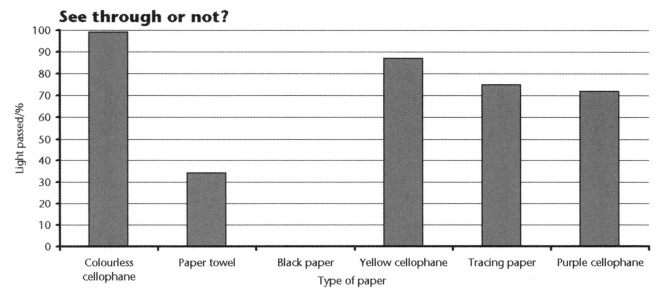

Questions

1. Talk about and write down any things you can think of that you should do to make the test fair.

2. Which paper let the most light through?

3. Which paper blocked the most light? Explain how you decided this from the results.

4. Which sample of paper is being measured on the picture of the datalogger?

5. Fill in this table, putting the papers in the correct order of transparency, with the most transparent first.

Type of paper	Light passed/%

HANDLING SCIENCE DATA YEAR 3

SNAKEY MAGNETS

> ***National Curriculum Science*** KS2 PoS Sc4: 2a
> ***QCA Science*** Unit 3E: Magnets and springs
> ***Scottish 5–14 Guidelines*** Energy and forces: Forces and their effects – Level B

HOW TO GATHER THE DATA

You will need a range of magnets for this activity – most schools have many types, collected over the years. Try to find different shapes or types of magnet; if you use identical new magnets, all the children will get the same result. With very strong magnets, children can have difficulty keeping the paper clips stretched out in a snake; and be warned that children of a more devious nature may try to 'fool' you (not a chance!) by connecting all the paper clips together and pretending they are magnetised!

Children can display their own results as a drawing, as long as they count and draw the correct number of clips. (This method of recording is suitable for a wide range of abilities.) They can then, if you wish, make a pictogram of paper clips for a group of results.

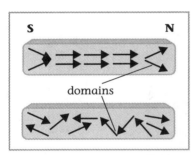

domains

THE SCIENCE BEHIND THE DATA

A magnet is an object able to exert a force of attraction on magnetic materials. The type of magnetism tested and used in the primary school is technically 'ferromagnetism'. Contrary to popular belief, not all metals are magnetic: aluminium and copper, for example, are not magnetic. Only iron, nickel and cobalt are powerfully magnetic. Steel is mainly iron, so anything made from steel can be magnetic. (Note that 'copper' coins minted now are not made from pure copper: they contain nickel and iron, so are magnetic!)

A magnetic material can be thought of being made up of lots of tiny magnets called 'domains'. When the material is magnetised, all the domains line up to point the same way, causing a magnetic 'field' extending beyond the magnet itself (the field gets weaker further away from the magnet).

When a magnet (or magnetised material) is 'demagnetised', the domains point in lots of different directions and cancel each other out. Dropping, banging or heating a magnet will demagnetise the material. To preserve their magnetism, magnets should be stored in pairs with opposite poles attracting one another.

When a piece of steel, such as a paper clip, is put near a magnet, the domains in the steel line up as in the magnet, so it will always be attracted. The materials attracted to a magnet become temporary magnets themselves – this is 'induced' magnetism. This effect can be seen in any piece of steel (such as additional paper clips) placed within the magnetic field. But the induced magnetic strength weakens further away from the magnet, and will eventually be too weak to affect any more paper clips. When the paper clips are taken away from the magnetic field the domains become random again and the magnetism is lost (though sometimes some magnetism may be retained).

Answers

1. Angie.
2. Hers had the most paper clips attached.
3. Davina.
4. Hers had the fewest paper clips attached.
5. Karen and Immi (provided the paper clips were identical).
6. The paper clips should have been the same size and made from the same material. ('The same magnet' is not a correct answer.)
7. They are steel, which is a magnetic material.
8. The magnet made each paper clip into a magnet that attracted the next paper clip, and so on.
9. They would not stick. Plastic is not magnetic.
10. They would stick. The magnetic force can operate through other materials (eg a strong magnet under a table can move magnetic objects on top of the table).

Snakey magnets

Some children were having a competition to find out who had the strongest magnet. They were making snakes of paper clips on their table.

Each child had to drag as many paper clips as possible with a magnet. The children had to be very careful when they moved the magnets.

When they had made the longest snake possible, each child counted how many paper clips he or she could drag.

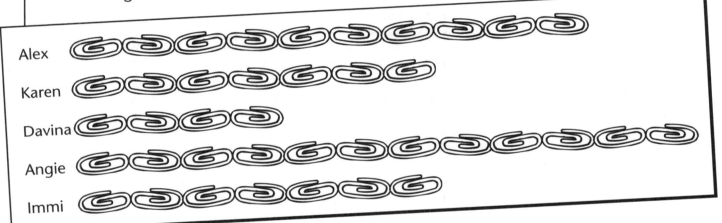

Questions

1. Who had the strongest magnet?

2. How do the results tell you that?

3. Who had the weakest magnet?

4. How do you know?

5. Which two children had magnets with the same strength?

6. Name two things the children should have kept the same to make the competition fair.

7. Why did the paper clips stick to the magnet?

8. Can you explain why more than one paper clip stuck to the magnet?

9. What would happen if the children used plastic paper clips?

10. What would happen if the children used plastic-coated steel paper clips?

HANDLING SCIENCE DATA YEAR 3

SPRINGY SCIENCE

> *National Curriculum Science* KS2 PoS Sc4: 2d, 2e
> *QCA Science* Unit E: Magnets and springs
> *Scottish 5–14 Guidelines* Energy and forces: Forces and their effects – Level B

HOW TO GATHER THE DATA

This investigation is interesting because most experiments with springs stretch them, though similar data can be obtained by stretching elastics (see the activity 'Stretching tights' on page 37). This is also a lot more fun to carry out!

When carrying out this investigation, children might find it difficult to judge the highest point. A possible solution would be to have a background of coloured bands that children can look at as the ball reaches its peak and use as a guide. Alternatively, put the spring at an angle (say 45°) and measure how far the ball goes before it first lands – very good fun!

Questions 1–5 are fairly straightforward, but from Question 6 onwards the children will need to be quite experienced investigators. Identifying trends is quite a high-level skill, but the one anomalous result here should be identified by most children. For those who find describing a trend difficult and need support with this skill, we have found that making a simple rhythm or jingle provides a scaffold on which children can structure their response. For example: 'The bigger the squash, the higher the jump…' – the first part is what you have changed, the second is what you have measured. This support is extremely effective in developing clear, concise thinking and expression of ideas. It helps the children to focus on the essentials of the investigation, deciding on a trend and expressing it (as discussed in the Introduction, page 6).

Question 7 is designed to be open-ended. Often these types of questions lead you to ideas for other investigations. The format links to planning grids (one is provided on photocopiable resource page 62), which again are extremely effective as scaffolding for the structure of an investigation.

Answers

1. 6cm
2. Zero (no squash).
3. 4cm squash (it does not follow the trend).
4. Repeat this one.
5. About 40cm.
6. The greater the squash, the higher the jump.
7. Look for any investigation question that involves launching different balls. Children might suggest different masses, sizes or materials – anything is OK, whether it would produce a varied set of results or not. If they choose mass then ideally the balls should be the same size, but they do not have to be to get a set of results (very large balls will not work on a small spring, but there is no reason why the children cannot find that out for themselves and then explain the problems to you – they are learning to be critical investigators). Don't necessarily dismiss things that might seem 'silly' to us (such as the colour of the ball): would a 7- or 8-year-old know for certain whether colour makes a difference or not?

THE SCIENCE BEHIND THE DATA

In all materials there are both attractive and repulsive forces operating between the particles. In a solid these opposing forces are balanced and hold the particles in a fixed position. In a spring the particles of metal (or other material) have strong forces operating between them: if you try to squeeze the particles closer, the repulsive forces between the particles become stronger and the particles tend to move apart again. Likewise, if you try to pull the particles apart, the repulsive forces become weaker, so the attractive forces become relatively stronger and tend to pull the particles back together. Whichever way you try to distort the shape of the spring, the forces will act against you and pull or push the spring back into shape. The direction of this force as the spring returns to shape can make an object (in this experiment, the ball) move in that direction.

Springy science

Daniel was playing with a spring and was excited when he made it bounce in the air. The children wanted to investigate this. Their teacher, Miss Jones, said that she had some plastic balls they could launch with the springs.

One group decided they would change how far they squashed the spring to see how high the ball jumped.

This is a graph of their results:

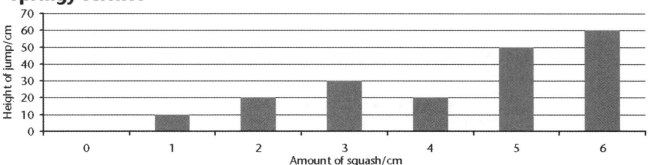

Questions

1. Which squash gave the biggest jump?

2. Which squash gave no jump?

3. Maya said one result was wrong. Which one do you think she meant?

4. What should Maya do about that result?

5. What do you think the height of that jump should be?

6. How does the amount of squash affect the height of the jump?

7. Describe an investigation the children could do with different balls and the spring. In your plan you should include these things:

- what you are trying to find out – your question
- what you will change each time
- what you will measure each time
- what you should keep the same each time
- a prediction of what you think will happen
- a blank table showing the headings and units
- a blank graph showing the labelled axes
- a prediction of what the graph will look like.

HANDLING SCIENCE DATA YEAR 3

SUNDIAL

National Curriculum Science KS2 PoS Sc4: 3b and 4b
QCA Science Unit 3F: Light and shadows
Scottish 5–14 Guidelines Earth and space: Earth in space – Level A/B

HOW TO GATHER THE DATA

A good preliminary activity is to ask the children (before they go out) to draw what they think they will see when they go into the sunshine. Ask them to draw the positions of the Sun, themselves and their shadows. After they have been outside and seen this, ask them to draw the scene again; this encourages the children to think about the angles and straight lines that are important for shadows. It reinforces two ideas: the need for observation of the world, and the value of gathering evidence.

For the investigation, choose a fine sunny day and put a rounders post (or similar) in the playground where it will not be disturbed. Ask the children to make a chalk mark along the shadow to mark it, and then to measure the length of the shadow with a tape measure, metre rule or trundle wheel. Repeat this, recording the length of the shadow at successive times during the day – you need to start as early in the day as possible and finish as late as possible.

It would be useful to have a further set of results recorded at a different time of year to make comparisons. This would also be an excellent investigation with which to share results from different parts of the world, if you have Internet partner schools. Midday at the equator gives no shadow (at midsummer). The southern hemisphere gives southerly shadows; the northern hemisphere gives northerly shadows. Remember that daylight saving time (BST) operates in summer in the UK, so the shortest shadow occurs at 1pm.

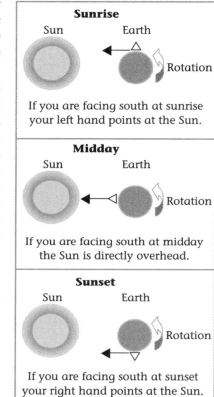

Sunrise

If you are facing south at sunrise your left hand points at the Sun.

Midday

If you are facing south at midday the Sun is directly overhead.

Sunset

If you are facing south at sunset your right hand points at the Sun.

THE SCIENCE BEHIND THE DATA

Light travels in straight lines. Any opaque object will cast a shadow the same shape as the object, because light cannot go through it or bend around it. Some children think that a shadow is a 'thing' in itself and not simply darkness (the absence of light).

The shadow of the sundial in the experiment appears to move because the Earth is rotating about its own axis. This produces the *apparent* movement of the Sun. The diagrams (see above right) show the view from above the north pole, with someone standing at the equator.

This concept can be very difficult for children to grasp, but it can be modelled using a globe with a piece of Blu-tack (1cm tall) attached and a light source such as an OHP. When you have the OHP and globe lined up at approximately the same heights (make minor adjustments to get the best effect), turn the globe anticlockwise and the shadow will change both its direction and length as a sundial does. This demonstrates that the changes in a shadow can be produced by the rotation of the Earth while the Sun stays still.

Answers
1. A bar graph.
2. The shadow gets shorter up to 1pm, then it gets longer.
3. 1pm
4. The Sun is at its highest in the sky.
5. A line drawn longer than the line for 3pm and to the right on the diagram. A bar on the graph at 4pm, higher than the bar for 3pm.
6. It follows a smooth trend or pattern.
7. An arrow pointing back from the line of the shadow formed at 2pm.

Sundial

On a sunny day Rajan, Anita and Tara took a rounders post into the playground to measure its shadow during the course of the day. They started at 9 o'clock in the morning and finished at 3pm. Every hour they recorded the length and position of the shadow.

They recorded their results on a diagram:

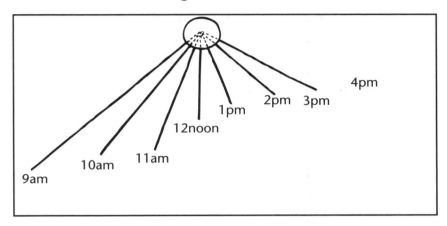

Then they made a graph of their results:

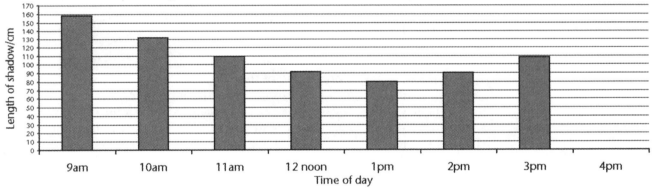

Questions

1. What type of graph did the children draw?

2. Describe in detail what happens to the length of the shadow as the day goes on.

3. When was the shadow at its shortest?

4. Why do you think the shadow is shorter then than at any other time?

5. On both the diagram and the graph, draw a result to show the length of the shadow at 4pm.

6. How does the graph show that the children have made their measurements correctly?

7. On the diagram, draw an arrow pointing towards the Sun at 2pm.

HANDLING SCIENCE DATA YEAR 3

TORCH SHADOWS

National Curriculum Science KS2 PoS Sc4 3a,b
QCA Science Unit 3F: Light and shadows
Scottish 5–14 Guidelines Energy and forces: Properties and uses of energy – Level C

HOW TO GATHER THE DATA

This investigation can be carried out with any opaque object to cast the shadow (small batteries are readily available and stand up quite easily), but it works better with short objects. Don't use a full-sized pencil!

You'll also need to take considerable care in making measurements; keeping the distance from torch to object the same while changing the angle is important, which the children do not always appreciate. This may well be better as a whole-class demonstration or a closely supervised group activity. A board protractor will help with changing the angles consistently – the children do not need to know about angles, just to use it as a positional guide.

When the children are drawing their own graphs, they can use photocopiable resource page 62 as a set of prepared axes (which they will need to label as appropriate).

THE SCIENCE BEHIND THE DATA

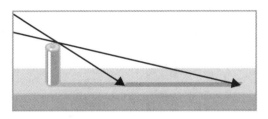

Light travels in straight lines. It cannot bend around corners. Any opaque object placed between a light source and a surface onto which it shines will cast a shadow with the same shape as that of the object . A shadow always appears on the opposite side of the object from the light source, because the light is travelling from the source towards (and past) the object. As the light hits the object it is blocked (reflected away), so there is less light immediately behind the object than there is in front or to the side of it. This absence of light is the shadow. Some children think that a shadow is a 'thing' in itself, but it is simply the absence of light.

The shadow of the battery in the experiment changes in length for two reasons: the angle of the torch is changing, and light travels in straight lines. You can model this by drawing a straight line (or using art straws) from the light source to the top of the object and then on to the desk. As you change the angle of the line, the length of the shadow changes.

Answers

1. The battery is opaque/blocks the light.
2. The same shape as the object (battery-shaped).
3. A shadow has the same shape as the object producing it.
4.

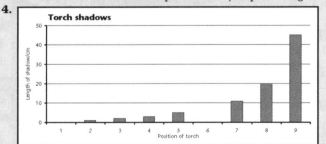

5. The missing bar should be between 6cm and 10cm.
6. The lower the torch, the longer the shadow/the higher the torch, the shorter the shadow. (Encourage the children to mention both the position of the torch and the length of the shadow, not simply say 'It gets longer.')
7. There is a smooth change in the results.
8. The shadow will be on the opposite side of the battery from the torch, but the shadow's lengths will not change.
9. A shadow will always be on the opposite side of the object from the light source.

Torch shadows

Javed was using a torch to make shadows with different objects. He noticed that when he moved the torch the size of the shadow changed. He set up a proper investigation to try and find a pattern.

Diagram of set up

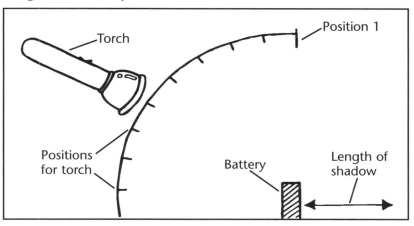

Javed used a battery as an object to make the shadow, and set up the torch at different positions. Each time, he measured the length of the shadow.

Here is the table of his results, but one result is missing.

Position of lamp	Length of shadow/cm
1	0
2	1
3	2
4	3
5	5
6	
7	11
8	20
9	45

Questions

1. Why did the battery have a shadow?

2. What shape was the shadow?

3. Explain your answer to question 2.

4. Draw a bar graph of the results in the table.

5. Fill in the missing bar for position 6.

6. What happens to the length of the shadow as Javed changes the position of the torch?

7. This is a tricky investigation to get accurate results in. How do Javed's results show that he was careful?

8. What will happen to the position of the shadow if Javed moves the torch to the other side of the battery?

9. Explain your answer to question 8.

HANDLING SCIENCE DATA YEAR 3

Planning sheet

Use this sheet to plan an investigation.

Our question: _____

_____

My prediction is: _____

_____

What we will change: _____

_____

What we will measure: _____

_____

What we will keep the same: _____

_____

_____

_____

Our results:

Graph paper

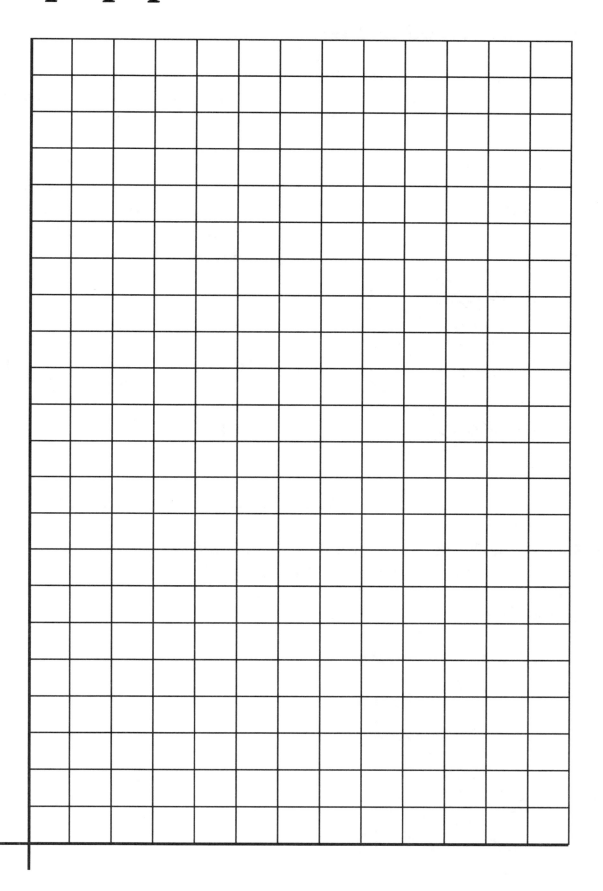

How to grow seeds in a germination sandwich

It's easy to grow seeds in a germination sandwich, so you can watch them germinate and grow. You will need: a wooden frame, vermiculite, seeds, a Perspex cover, elastic bands, a bucket of water.

1. Lay the empty frame on a table, and fill it with vermiculite.

2. Place some seeds in the vermiculite near the top of the frame, so they have room for their roots to grow. Be careful not to squash the seeds, and don't put too many in the frame.

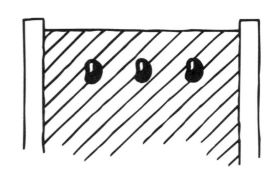

3. Place the Perspex cover over the frame and secure it with elastic bands. This will let you see how the seeds grow.

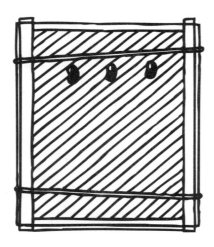

4. Stand the germination sandwich up in a tank of water, and wait for the seeds to start growing.

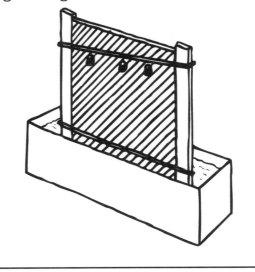